THE CELL BLOCK PRESENTS…

The Mob

Published by: The Cell Block™

The Cell Block
P.O. Box 1025
Rancho Cordova, CA 95741

Website: thecellblock.net
Facebook/thecellblockofficial
Instagram: @mikeenemigo
Corrlinks: info@thecellblock.net

Copyright ©2022, by Boss Mafi

Cover Design: Mike Enemigo

Send comments, reviews, interview and business
inquiries to: info@thecellblock.net

PROLOGUE

My mind went blank when I first heard my bro Dre got smoked. I just couldn't believe it. I remember thinking, how could the Mac be dead? I was just with bruh last week! All of our plans had come together and were flourishing beyond what we could have ever imagined. And to top it off, we were just getting started.

In a way, I blame myself, because I had Dre go out to K.C. In an effort to expand our enterprise by linking up with Fat Tone; the same way I sent the Mob Figgaz to Ohio to link with Ampichino. Many things about Dre's death bothered me, but the questions that burned within me the most were: who and why? The Kansas City press and police had formed their own theories about what had transpired; but the streets talk, and the Mob was getting different info.

We had already found out who ordered the hit; it was most definitely Fat Tone. Everyone from the streets knew Fat Tone was a hitter out there in K.C. That was one of the main reasons I wanted to tie him into the Mob's operations.

But Fat Tone fucked up: he took out a family member. In other words, he signed his own death certificate and instantly became a Dead Nigga Walkin'. Now that we knew who called the hit, the task at hand shifted to finding out who the trigger man was.

Word on the streets was that Fat Tone had felt Dre'd overstepped his boundaries in Kansas City, and they had an exchange of words. We received different variations of what these words were about, but the cause and content of them were irrelevant: Dre was a Bay Boss, and his death wouldn't go unanswered. The whole Mob was ready to kill anyone and everybody who had anything to do with It.

In the Mob, it's all about loyalty. We push the ethic of "no man left behind." If a Mob brother gets locked up, he's well taken care of. If a Mob brother gets smoked, his family is taken care of and his death avenged without exception.

Fat Tone sent word denying that he and his goons had any involvement with Dre's death, but none of that was flying with the Mob. Our research gave us the answers we were looking for. The fact was, we had multiple sources that gave us the same script about who was responsible for Dre's death, and when it comes to the Mob, you take one of ours, you'll be lucky if we only take two of yours....

CHAPTER 1

1986 …

Everybody always asks me how I got the name "Paperboy," or why I go by Paperboy. Paperboy is a name I got way back in the day, when I was only 13 years old.

I come from extreme poverty and grew up in a little city in the Bay Area of Cali called Pittsburg. These days, Pittsburg is better known as 'the P', or 'P-World.'

I was raised in the 80s. We consider those days 'the Crack Era'. Back then, the streets of the Bay Area were flooded with crack rock. It was to the point that, in the hood, everybody's momma and daddy was a smoker. Mine was no exception; she was hooked! Because of this, we had it bad. By 'we' I mean my lil' bro and lil' sis, as well as myself.

Now, some of y'all may be too young to remember when food stamps came in booklets and were "bills", like cash. Back in my day, though, that's how it was. These days, food stamps go straight onto EBT cards. This is because, in the 80s, D-Boys started accepting food stamps as payment for dope.

Mind you, since food stamps weren't real 'cash money', D-Boys would only accept them at half-price. So a five-dollar rock would cost a smoker ten dollars' worth of food stamps, feel me?

That's how the game worked back then. So D-Boy's didn't only have stacks of real money, they also had stacks of food stamps. And when I say stacks of food stamps, I mean fat stacks! Believe it or not, food stamps were such a factor in the dope game, even the plug would accept them when the block bleeders came to re-up!

In the hood, most of the crackheads were on welfare, especially the single mothers. The addiction was so strong that obtaining the drug would come even before feeding their children or paying the bills. So, as soon as they would get their food stamps, they would go straight to the dope-man and start spending.

The government knew this was a problem they had to solve. So, they eventually tried doing so by putting food stamps on EBT cards. Now, that might have put a speed bump in the game, but it didn't stop nothing, because, every time a D-Boy needed some groceries, the crackhead would make it happen!

Anyway, around the first of every month, my momma would get her food stamps and go straight to one of the dope-boys on our block. She wouldn't blow it all on rock, though, she would grab some groceries for the house – mostly Top Ramens. But with three kids in the house, that Top Ramen, and whatever else we had to eat, wouldn't last very long. Halfway through the month, the fridge would be empty and the cupboards bare. That's where I came into play. As the oldest, I felt it was my responsibility to make sure my younger siblings didn't go without, so I jumped off the porch and hit the streets.

At 13 years old, there were not many kids my age running the streets, so naturally I hung around the older crowd. They knew my situation. In fact, they were the ones serving my momma crack. These older niggas looked at me like a lil' bro and welcomed me up under the wing of El Pueblo Mob, aka the Lo Mob, which was named after the "El Pueblo Housing Project" where we all lived, and where we grew up.

I remember being out on the block with the older cats, posted up, when my mom would slide through to get her rock. She would get her fix, then say something slick like, "Y'all betta be takin' care of my boy out here!" to which they'd reply with something like, "Oh, you know he always gon' be good out here wit' us!" Then my momma would smash off to get high. …

CHAPTER 2

At first, I'd do whatever I could to make money, such as steal bikes and sell them. Once I stole a leaf blower from a city worker's truck and would blow leaves off yards for five dollars each. Shit, I'd even rob the water fountain at the police station for all the silver change, and cash it in for what it added up to in bills. I was a natural hustler, so I'd always find ways to make money.

I remember one time, I saw a box of pit bull puppies outside the local market. Some guy was giving them away, free. I approached him and asked if I could have the whole box. He thought I was joking, laughed, and asked if I was serious. "Hell, yeah, I'm serious. I want the whole box," I told him. Once he realized I wasn't joking, he asked if my mom would be OK with me bringing a whole box of puppies to the house. I told him straight up: "I'm not going to keep em', I'm gonna sell em'."

He nodded his head as he took this in for a second, then said: "I respect that. They're all yours."

I carried the whole box home with a big-ass grin on my face, because I knew I was about to make some money. I already knew where I'd sell them, I just had to figure out how much I could actually get for each one. I had no idea what they went for, so I decided I'd ask for twenty dollars each.

The next day I took the puppies to the city park, which was in the next hood over – Parkside. It was baseball season, and the park was flooded with people. This is a big-ass park with about six or seven baseball fields, three parking lots, a basketball court, two playgrounds, and a mini-stage that can be used for a number of things. During the day, the park looks nice and friendly, but don't let that fool you. During the night, the police won't even go in there unless they absolutely have to.

Anyway, I hit the park with about eight pups. I knew they were pits, but I didn't know what kind of pits they were until I asked someone if he wanted to buy a pit, and he said, "Oh, you got you some Red Noses, huh? How much you want?" I told him twenty dollars, and he said "Sold!" Then he grabbed an all-white female and said he was gonna name her Remy.

I ended up selling all of them for twenty bucks each in about forty-five minutes or so. Now, that might not seem like much to you, but to a 13-year-old kid from the ghetto, I was balling! Not for long, of course; my money always went straight to buying food and paying bills for the house. Not that I minded; shit, that's the reason I was out there hustling in the first place. Besides, I really didn't have much of a choice. I can't even begin to tell you how many times our water or power was shut off, or we ran out of food; it seemed like every other month. I remember jumping over the fence into the neighbor's backyard and running an extension cord to the outlet in the back of their house. To this day, I wonder if they ever figured it out. On those months, their electric bill had to be sky-high.

Regardless, no matter what, I always did my best to make sure the bills were paid and there was something on the table for my little bro and sis. However, in the few times I wasn't able to make something happen, and times got real bad, my mom would step up to the plate. I remember her pushing whole grocery carts full of food right out the store without paying. She also had a little scheme. She would go into a store, grab an expensive item, then take it straight to the customer service and return it.

She would run some drag about how she couldn't find the receipt, and they would give her money. I guess you could do that one time per store, but you had to show ID. They would log you into their computer, and you couldn't return anything to their store without a receipt again. She always had me with her when she'd do it, I guess to throw them off. There were times when we'd hit multiple stores in multiple cities, all in one day.

CHAPTER 3

One day I was outside, chilling, in front of my spot, when my little sister's friend's mom pulled up. She was there to pick up my sister for her daughter's birthday party. The lady stepped out of her soccer-mom van and was talking to my mom about what time she'd have my little sister home. Then she asked my mom a question that caught my attention: "Do you know anybody who might be interested in doing a paper route in this area?" I guess there was too much violence in the neighborhood and people kept quitting.

I instantly butted in: "I'll do it." My mom and the lady looked at me like I was crazy. I paid their looks no mind and kept going: "I can do it on my bike."

The lady smiled at me and said, "I wouldn't mind, I really need to find someone to do it, but you're too young." Then she looked at my mom: "Would you be OK with him doing it?"

My mom didn't care what I did. She knew I was in the streets all day, every day. So, of course I wasn't surprised when she said, "Yeah, I would be OK with him doing it."

The lady explained to my mom that they could make it happen, as long as she – my mom – looked like the one who was actually hired on the paperwork. My mom agreed, and when the lady brought my sister home from the party, they filled out the necessary paperwork and made everything official.

On my first day, a truck pulled up and dropped off a couple stacks of newspapers, a bag of rubber bands, a list of addresses to where the papers were to be delivered, and the bag that went over my head with a pouch in the front and a pouch in the back to hold the papers while I passed them out. I didn't waste any time. I quickly started rolling papers and rubber-banding them. When I was done, I put them in the two pouches.

I put the thing over my head with the papers, jumped on my bike, and started making my rounds. At first, I had to stop in front of every house before tossing the paper onto the doorstep. But after hitting a few streets, I started to figure out how to coast down the block and throw the paper at the same time. The trick was to hit the front door, then the paper would land right on the doormat.

While I was in the process of delivering papers, random people kept asking me if I had any extras. A few people even offered me a dollar for one. I kept saying no, because I didn't think I did. But once I was done with my route, I realized I did have some extras, so I backtracked, looking for everyone who had asked for one.

I was only able to find a couple of the people who'd initially asked, so I decided to start doing the asking. I was determined to sell them all, so I asked everyone I saw. I eventually sold every extra paper and made about $10, so from that day forward, I knew exactly how many extras I had, so every time someone would ask, "Do you have an extra paper?" I would respond with a question of my own: Do you have a dollar for it?

One day I was just starting to make my rounds, when I ran into Kaydah. He was one of the reputables from my hood. He ended up asking me if I had an extra paper, so I asked him if he had a dollar. He started laughing and said, "OK, youngsta', I see you really are a paperboy."

"Yup, I sure am," I responded. As he handed me the dollar, he said, "From now on, that's your name 'round here – Paperboy!"

Shit, he wasn't lying, either. Next thing I knew, the whole hood was calling me Paperboy. So by hustling extra papers and trying to make a few dollars, I ended up with a name: Paperboy. In fact, Kaydah was known for giving youngsters in the hood their name. There was a whole squad of us "Bay Bay's" kids that got our name from Kaydah. Like I said, he was a factor in the Lo. So when he gave you a name, it stuck.

CHAPTER 4

By the time I was 14, I was no longer slinging newspapers. I had elevated to the crack game. Crackheads were always asking me if I had rocks for sale, and, well, I got tired of sending that money to someone else. It was time for me to get my hands on some work, and really start taking care of my family. My mom's drug addiction was getting worse. So the way I seen it, I really didn't have a choice! Our struggle was the ugliest it'd ever been, so I had to step up to the plate and start pitching.

It was bound to happen anyway. My family tree was known to produce hustlas, most notably my uncle, Felix Mitchell, aka Felix the Cat. For those of y'all who don't know, my uncle is a legend and will forever be known as a Bay Boss. He was the leader of the '69 M.O.B. (My Other Brother) in Oakland. He sold heroin until the crack era hit in the 80s, then he bubbled mostly off of crack. Shit, he was bringing in right around five million a year, then eventually got caught up and was sentenced to life in '85. Then in '86, some sucka killed him in Leavenworth penitentiary, in Kansas. Gone but not forgotten. The hustle that ran through his veins, runs through mine.

One thing I heard over and over while growing up was how much I reminded everybody of my uncle. Although I was too young to realize it, at 14 years old, I was already walking in his footsteps. I had set my mind on selling crack, and once I set my mind to something, ain't no stopping me.

So, here I was, on a mission to come up on a bundle I could flip. I was chopping it up with my boy Nell on the way home from school, when I told him: "These smokers keep trying to buy rock from me, so I'm trying to come up on some."

He looked at me all funny, and in a whisper, said, "I can get you some."

There was literally nobody around, but I still whispered back, "How? Can you get it right now?"

He explained how he was snooping around his dad's room and found a stack of shoeboxes full of rocks in the closet. He said he could snatch some, and his dad would never know. That next morning, I was waiting for him in front of my spot so we could push to school together. I was waiting and waiting. But he wasn't showing up. I figured he chickened out, so I walked off. I was halfway down the block, when I heard my name called. I looked back and saw his ass walking towards me hella fast. I turned around and headed back towards him, wondering if he had brought anything. When we met up, he handed me an ice cream wrapper with five rocks inside of it, then started looking around all nervous and shit.

I quickly went back to my house to hide the bundle in my room, and when I came out, Nell looked a lot calmer. After school, I went straight home, grabbed the bundle, grabbed my bike, and hit the streets. At the end of my block, I saw a tomboy named Kendra. She was always out there getting money, night and day. I headed her way.

When I pulled up on her, she was smoking a blunt and had Too Short's "Born to Mack" slapping out of her boom box. Through an exhale, she said, "What you want, Paperboy?"

I smiled as I blurted out, "I got some rocks, can you sell 'em for me?"

Through another exhale, she said, "Lil' boy, you ain't got no damn rocks." So I just pulled out the ice-cream wrapper and handed it to her.

She grabbed it, looked at the rocks inside, and handed it right back. She hit the blunt a couple times without saying anything, then she finally said: "Check it out, Paperboy. In these streets, you gotta get yo' own money."

I instantly felt stupid. I don't even know why I asked her in the first place. "Alright, that's what I'ma do," I told her.

I was posted on the block with Kendra for a cool minute listening to the Too Short tape, then a basehead came slow-draggin' up. I looked at Kendra, and she said, "Go 'head, that one's yo's." I'd been around long enough to know how it worked, so when he got closer, I hit him up.

"What you lookin' for?"

The basehead looked back and forth between Kendra and me and said, "A nickel piece." I pulled out my ice cream wrapper, did the transaction, and he was gone.

After he left, Kendra gave me some game on keeping a few rocks in my mouth under my tongue, and the rest hidden elsewhere, away from where we were at. She said, "If the pigs pull up trippin', swallow em'." After I told her I understood, she went on about how I would have to throw them back up after the pigs left. She explained that I might even have to drink milk to make them float in my stomach, that way they'd come back up easier.

I just shrugged my shoulders and said, "I can do that."

CHAPTER 5

Being that I was so anxious to get money, all that standing around waiting for baseheads wasn't working for me, so I jumped on my bike and told Kendra: "I'ma go find me some baseheads."

She started laughing, and said: "That's right, boy, get on yo' paper chase then."

I rode around, pulling up on anyone who even resembled a crackhead. Before I knew it, all my rocks were gone. Shit, it couldn't have taken me longer than an hour.

Once I was out of work, I headed back to the block. I pulled right back up on Kendra and said: "I got 'em off."

She looked at me with a confused look on her face. "All of 'em?" she asked.

"Yup, all of 'em."

She smiled approval with her gold teeth on full display, and said, "OK, Paperboy, get out there and get it, then."

I started telling her how I'd pulled up on every knock I'd seen, when she interrupted me, and asked, "So, you ready for a double-up, right?"

"What's a double-up?" I asked.

She explained that, whatever amount of money I spent, I would get enough rock to double it. I couldn't believe my ears; of course I wanted to double my money! I pulled the twenty-five dollars out of my pocket, and as I handed it to her I said, "You betta know I want a double-up!"

She grabbed the money, ran into her spot, and came out with my next bundle. I got on my bike, but before I smashed off to grind, I said, "So we can do this double-up every time?"

"Hell, yeah," she said. "And before you know it, you'll have enough for a real sack." With that in mind, I peeled off in search of some more baseheads to serve.

I took School Street and headed towards the city park. When I got there, I saw a couple of crackheads walking through the parking lot. They were headed towards the train tracks, so I sped up and headed their way. I pulled up on them with a skid, unexpectedly, which caused them to jump. I could tell it had irritated them, but I didn't care.

Y'all need some rock?" I asked.

They awkwardly looked at each other, then back at me. "Yeah, lil' man, we do. How much you got?"

I should've known better, but answered, "I got ten rocks."

Before the words fully escaped my mouth, one of the smokers snatched me off my bike, and the other ran through my pockets. "I'ma get y'all, niggas! You just watch!" I said, as they walked off with my bundle. They both just laughed as they crossed the tracks, going towards the Dime block.

I smashed back to the hood as fast as I could. When I got there, I seen Kendra, Kaydah, and a few other cats. I slid up completely out of breath: "Some punk-ass crackheads just jacked me for my bundle!"

Kendra erupted in laughter. When she finally stopped laughing, she said to Kaydah, "See" I told you Paperboy's lil' ass was out here pitchin'!"

Kaydah didn't think anything was funny. "Where they at?" he asked, with his mean mug on. I explained that they'd crossed the tracks, headed towards the Dime. All he said after that was, "Jump in!" We jumped into Kaydah's Box Chev' five deep, as he gassed off slappin' "Let's Slide" by the Click.

We floated down School Street, bent a right on Railroad headed downtown. We pulled up to the light, made a left on 10th Street (the Dime), and another quick left towards the other side of the tracks. We coasted down the block, bent a right, and I spotted them. "There they go!" I yelled.

Kaydah flew right up on them, and all four doors flew open. The crackheads froze up, and before they knew it, they were surrounded. They both looked at me and knew exactly what time it was. The one that ran through my pockets dug into his and pulled out my bundle. He must've known big bruh, because he said: "Ey, Kaydah, I didn't know the kid was wit' you, man."

Kaydah grabbed my bundle with one hand, slapped the smoker with the other, and said: "Now you do."

As soon as Kaydah slapped the first one, Kendra punched the other, then all five of us stomped they bitch-ass out.

CHAPTER 6

We smashed back to the Lo and started unloading out of Kaydah's whip. "Check it out, lil' nigga," Kaydah spoke, obviously referring to me.

"What's good, big bruh?" I asked.

"If you're gonna be out here pitchin' in these streets, I'ma make sure you're game-tight and understand the in's and out's of the dope game! … So, stop by the crib after school tomorrow, and I'll educate you properly on this Mob shit!" Kaydah stated, as he dismissed me with a wave of his hand. Then he gassed off.

Kaydah was a real nigga, and at that young age I admired him greatly, wanting to be a boss just as he was. So of course, I was excited that my idol wanted to lace me up like some new Jordans. While other kids my age were worried about candy and chasing skirts, I was focused on getting my money and becoming a boss.

After school got out the next day, I made my way through Parkside on my way to the hood and Kaydah's spot. It was hotter than hell, so I stopped at

Parkside Market to grab a soda. "What's up, lil' man?" asked Jamal, recognizing me as I walked in. He and his family owned the market, and if you were a regular customer, he greeted you as if you were family.

"What's poppin', Jamal? That heat ain't no joke! I need a soda," I responded. Once I saw he was working the register, I knew I'd get it for free. He didn't work the register much, but when he did, he always hooked me up like that. I grabbed a Pepsi and pushed up to the counter: "It's on the house, my man, you know the deal!" Jamal stated with a wink.

"Good lookin' out, Jamal. I'll catch you later." I thanked him as I exited and continued my mission.

As I hit Kaydah's block, a bum named Carlos, aka the Can Man (he got it going door-to-door asking for cans), was sitting on the curb with a half-full forty-ounce of Old-E in his hand. "Aye, youngsta'! Remember me?" he asked, as his too-big clothes hung off him, and the smell of liquor reeked from his body.

It didn't matter if he seen you a million times, or for the first time; he asked EVERYBODY if they remembered him! I didn't even acknowledge him, and pushed to the end of the block, where Kaydah resided. As I approached, I had to stop and admire his Box Chev': dark brown paint, glossy with gold flakes sparkling in the sun, as his Gold-D's gleamed. At that moment, I made a silent vow that I would one day get myself a Box Chev' like that.

I pushed up to his spot and didn't know what door to knock on. Kaydah had two adjoining apartments, in which he had the separating wall knocked down, turning the two mid-sized apartments into one large suite. "That's what you call some ghetto-fabulous boss shit!" he later told me, when I asked him about it.

Kaydah was a General in the projects, and well respected. He loved his hood and every aspect of it. He would talk to smokers on the street as if they were friends. He was a hustla' in every sense of the word, selling weight and pitching stones. No amount of money was too little for him: "It all adds up the same; a million in big bills or a million in singles, is still a million dollars!" I recall him preaching during one of our sessions. He was a man of the ghetto, that's why he didn't feel threatened by living in the middle of his trap.

I decided to knock on the door on the right.

Knock! Knock! Knock!

CHAPTER 7

I heard someone approaching, as his pit started barking; "Who dat?" Kaydah asked.

"It's me!" I responded, knowing he was expecting me.

"Who's me?" he asked in a chuckle.

"It's Paperboy," I answered. Instantly the scrape of deadbolts being unlocked sounded.

The door opened, and I was looking at the Mob-star the streets called Kaydah; he'd taken on the name back in the day when a couple out-a-town niggas tried to strip him for his prized possession – his Mob chain!

$$$$$

Kaydah inherited the Mob chain when his big bruh Ice was killed. Some niggas were scopin' Ice as he walked into the liquor store and peeped his fat-ass Mob medallion sparkling, as the diamonds danced in the sun. They were two deep and figured they'd be able to strong-arm Ice out his chain.

The niggas waited for him to walk out; then ran up on him with guns drawn and demanded him to come off his chain. But Ice was a stone-cold killa' (hence the name Ice), and his pride wouldn't allow him to come off of not even a dollar he possessed. You would have to kill him or die trying, point-blank-period!

So off the top he refused their demands: "You got me fucked up! I ain't comin' off shit!" he spat.

"You got ten seconds to come off yo' chain, before I smack you for it. Ten ... nine ... seven ...," one of the Jack-Boys started counting down.

Before the nigga got to "one", Ice had pulled the pistol off his hip like an old western gun slinger and started shooting!

Boom! Boom! Boom!

But it was two against one, and as soon as he started shooting, the Jack-Boys started squeezing also.

Kaydah was sitting passenger in Ice's whip, twisting a blunt while the music was slapping. By the time he realized shit was poppin' off, it was too late. The gunfire stopped blazing, he hopped out the whip, and ran to his mentor's side.

"Sucka'-ass niggas thought they could lick me for my chain, younsta'," Ice mumbled to Kaydah, who was only known by his first name "Ivan" at the time. "We live for the Mob, and we die for the Mob! Go 'head and grab this Mob chain off my neck, lil' nigga, your time has come!" were his last words to Kaydah.

A few years later, Kaydah found himself in a similar situation: niggas standing in front of him tryna strip him for the Mob medallion. *We live for the Mob, and we die for the Mob*, he thought to himself, remembering his mentor's last words. Kaydah, too, being a stone-cold killa', would die before he came off the very chain his big bruh died for.

Not knowing Kaydah had an AK-47 leaned up on the other side of the green box where he was posted, they were caught by surprise when he swiftly spun around the box; he snatched the chop and started mowing them down where they stood. Them rookie-ass niggas didn't even get off a shot.

The streets referred to the "AK-47" as a "Kaydah," which is how Kaydah got his name.

$$$$$

The smell of marijuana and the speakers vibrating E-40 hit my senses at the same time. Kaydah smiled with his gold teeth: "My lil' nigga." He reached down and gave me dap. "Come in," he said, as he scanned the streets, then he shut the door.

I walked in and noticed his signature "Kaydah" with a banana clip sitting against the couch. He had a few piles of money on the coffee table, and a pile of rubber bands right next to them. On the floor was an opened duffel with stacks that were already counted and banded up. Then I glanced over to the kitchen and peeped two naked bitches sitting at the table with a mound of fish-scale and a couple boxes of Arm and Hammer.

"Yeah! You see that, Mob? Dope, money, and guns; that's how you get power, and that's how you keep power," he bragged, as he watched my observant eyes wander. "Come, help me count my 'fetti, while the bitches bake them cakes," he said, sitting down.

I sat down right next to him, and he handed me a stack of money so fat I had to put one hand on the bottom and another on the top just to hold it. I put it on the table in front of me as he spoke: "I knew the minute I saw yo' lil' ass hustlin' them newspapers, you'd be out here ballin' one day. Anybody can sell dope, but a real hustla' can sell anything and turn nuthin' into somethin'," he stated, as he resumed counting his money. "I just didn't expect you to jump off the porch so fast. But now that you got yo' feet wet, it's time for you to dive in," he admitted.

CHAPTER 8

"I would ask if you're ready, but you're here and actions speak volumes. So I'ma show you how to bleed the block for some real money, and in no time you'll be the youngest baller in the hood," Kaydah said with confidence.

"For real?" I asked, as I lit up like a lightbulb.

"On the Mob! Now, let's get to work, we're makin' five-G stacks," he said, pushing a pile of rubber-bands next to the money in front of me. Count each stack twice, and then band it up," he demanded.

After we finished counting all the money, and his duffel was full of five-G stacks, he told one of his bitches to bring him an eight-ball. She complied, handing him a lil' boulder tied up in a sandwich baggie. "Watch how I bust this down," he said, reaching under the couch, and pulling out a shoebox lid with a couple razors on it.

He took the eight-ball and began to skillfully bust it down, creating pieces. l watched intently, as he showed me how to bust it down without making it crumble. "You see how I'm doin' that?" he asked.

"Yeah, I see you!" I responded, feeling confident.

"Don't talk about it, be about it! Show me somethin'," Kaydah said, sliding the shoebox lid in front of me.

I instantly started chopping down a rock, mimicking his every move; "Like that?" I asked, knowing I was on point.

"Damn, lil' nigga, you a fast learner. I like that," he answered, as he gleamed like a proud father. "You're definitely a different breed, destined to be a factor in the dope game," he complimented, blowing my head up. "Shit, can you eye-ball the work already, too?" he joked, as he began to laugh. "Once you're a lil' more advanced, I'll have my bitches show you how to whip some shit up. But you gotta crawl before you walk, ya' dig?" he continued.

"Yeah! I can dig it," I said, nodding my head, but my eyes were on the naked bitches.

"Shit, if you got enough game, you might even be able to get you some pussy," he said, letting me know he peeped me hawking his bitches.

Instantly, both of them looked at me with their pearly whites on bright, obviously hearing big bruh's comment. I looked away, blushing, and Kaydah erupted in laughter.

We sat there and talked for hours, as Kaydah schooled me like he was a professor in a college auditorium. I hung onto his every word, as he unraveled the years of wisdom he'd gained from the harsh realities of the game. I didn't do much speaking myself, just continuously nodded my head as I soaked up the game that Kaydah was sprinkling me with. I was getting a Grade-A education in the D-

Game, and was about to grow up rapidly, with the help of my mentor. "It's gettin' late, lil' nigga, and I got business to maintain, so you better get home," Kaydah stated, ending the first of many sessions to come.

$$\$\$\$\$\$$

I hit the concrete jungle on the way to my house. The hot summer night made the air moist and sticky. As I made my way through the streets, I could hear the vulgar conversation of the crackheads who were posted under the beam of the full moon, and the gossip of the prostitutes who hid in the darkness, waiting for tricks to pull up. "What you doin' out here, lil' nigga?" I heard one of the hookers yell out. But I ignored the ho' and kept it pushin', headed towards my part of the projects.

By the time I hit my block, I heard the chaotic boom of subs pounding as a fly-ass 5.0 Mustang pulled up and parked. I recognized it as Kendra's bitch Unique's whip, and then I seen Kendra push up and jump in. Once they smashed off, the headlights no longer lit the block up, and it went back to being pitch-black.

All the street lights had been strategically shot out all through the hood. That's the way the Mob preferred it, because a thug was hard to see. Unless you know where to look, that is – there was a couple D-Boys tucked off in the shadows, working the night-shift, and waiting for a sell.

I got to my door and dipped in for the night.

The next day after getting schooled by big bruh, I had an eight-ball he put on me to get off; I'd learned the eight-ball was three and a half grams. I put that with the "Double-up" work that I'd got from Kendra, and I hit the streets to get my grind on.

I'd gotten off all my rocks in a few days, and was back to purchase my first bundle from Kaydah. Within a week I'd doubled up to seven grams, which at this point I knew was a quarter-ounce. I wasn't making any noise in the D-game, only curb-servin', but everyone knew I'd continue to graduate and would eventually be "The Man" one day. My demeanor showed it was inevitable, I just had to wait my turn, which would unfortunately come a lot faster than anybody could've ever imagined.

CHAPTER 9

1991 …

I remember my 18th birthday like it was yesterday. I was on my way to my nigga Dirt's house in my new whip, slapping Mac Dre's "California Livin'." *I need to get some beat in my trunk, and have my shit earthquakin'*, I thought, as I listened to the lyrics float out of my door speakers. My new whip was a 1981 Box Chev' sitting on Ds. Back then, if you was riding on Ds you was shittin'. I'd recently copped the whip from some mark-ass nigga that I sold weed to. He'd got caught slippin' while putting air in the tires at a gas station. Some cats he had funk with ran up on him with a banger and peeled him for his whip. A few days later, he found it with all the windows busted out.

At the time, I wasn't even driving yet, so I had to get a ride to take dude a half-ounce of Bomb. When I got there, I saw the whip with no windows, and asked him what had happened. That's when he mumbled how he got car-jacked for his shit. Now, I know dude had a lil' paper, so I asked him why he didn't put windows in. He told me he don't want to get caught slippin' again, now that his opps knew his car, so he wanted to sell it.

As soon as I heard that, I asked who his opps were, and found out they were some niggas I had funk with, too. I just shook my head, then said, "Fuck it, sell it to me. I'll slide in it."

Since it didn't have any windows, I ended up getting it for the low. The next morning, I slid to the window shop to get new windows put in. Now I was eating a lil' bit, but it's not like I was dumb ballin', so I only put the front and rear windows in. I wasn't tripping on the others, because I'd found someone that was selling some Ds. So it was either get all the windows, or only get the front and rear, but also the Ds. Of course, I did the responsible thing: I got the Ds!

Being young and wild, you know I had to stunt with some Ds on my shit. Besides, it was summer, so it just looked like the other windows were rolled down.

I needed a blunt, so I went to the hood spot where they knew me and didn't card me. As I pulled into the parking lot, I heard somebody thunder-knockin'. I looked over and saw that it was a black Honda that was also pulling into the parking lot. Now, this was a plaza, with a bunch of little stores and a grocery store. The Honda went and parked in one of the grocery store's parking spaces.

Being that I used to jack beat from cars and sell it, I knew all I needed was a flathead to pull the window back and I could reach in and unlock the door. After that I could pop the trunk with the release latch and snatch the beat.

The temptation was too much. The only thing my whip was missing, besides a few windows, was some slap. I had to get him.

I watched as the car parked, then some Asian cat got out and walked into the grocery store. One thing I know is, no one is in and out of a grocery store, which meant I had some time to work with.

I pulled into an empty parking space next to the Honda. I bounced out, hit the lick, and in about two minutes flat I had some beat for my shit. I went home, hooked my shit up, and was really feeling myself as I slid around town earth-quakin'.

So, like I was saying, it was my birthday, and I was on my way to the homie Dirt's house in my "new" whip. He was throwing a party that night and wanted me to come through. Dirt was from the West. I'd met him out there quite a few years back while staying in a homeless shelter called "Love a Child." We had gotten evicted, and with nowhere else to go, we ended up in that shelter. During that time, I'd met few niggas, but me and Dirt really clicked.

CHAPTER 10

I pulled up to Dirt's, bounced out, tucked my pistol, and dipped in. There was a gang of hoes dancing to Tupac's "2PACALYPSE NOW"; a few niggas I knew, and a few I didn't. I stepped in dumb-fresh from my hat to my shoes, so you know I had bitches peepin'. There was one, though, that was all the way locked in on me, big-ass smile and all. She was fly herself, so you know I had to return the smile and flash the gold ones.

I went to holla at Dirt. He wished me a happy birthday, then passed me a blunt and a bottle. As I was talking to bruh, I noticed ol' girl making her way over. I ended up meeting her halfway, and introduced myself. She was a thick Mexican chick with bright green eyes. She said her name was Abby.

We chopped it up real quick, but as I was walking off, I seen some cat push up on her, looking mad as hell. I thought it was funny, because I figured it was his bitch, but I knew I was gonna snatch her. Dirt knew it, too, and was shaking his head with a smile as I walked back over.

I asked Dirt what was up with Abby and Dude. He told me Dude's name was Marv, and that Abby had him sprung. As the night went on, I noticed Marv had Abby cuffed up next to him on the couch. I also noticed how she kept looking my way, so I said, "What you stuck on that couch fo'? Come kick it, enjoy yo' night." She hopped up instantly and strolled over next to me.

As soon as she did, Marv got up, sent a mug my way, and left. I couldn't do nothing but laugh at Dude; besides fuck his bitch, of course. The way she was all up on me, it was just a matter of time before that happened. Every time I looked into her eyes, she looked right back into mine like she wanted it right then and there.

We were on the couch flirting and shit, but it was time to turn up the heat. I said in her ear: "I'ma tryna fuck yo' sexy-ass all night tonight." She responded by jumping on my lap and kissing me. She must have felt my dick get hard, because she started slow grinding on it. I could feel her breathing harder while she kissed me, so I knew I had that pussy wet.

Out of nowhere, the front door swung open. Who walked in? You guessed it, Marv, just in time to see his girl all on my line. She slid off my lap and sat down at my side. Everybody got quiet. Marv looked at me like he wanted drama, so I bounced up on him.

"'Sup, nigga?" I said.

Now, I'm far from the type to funk over a bitch, but I can't help it if the next nigga wants to work with emotions over one, and go there with me. All I know is, he better be ready for what he's gonna have coming.

Dirt seen what was going on and pushed up on Marv: "Hold on, bruh. Yo' bitch chose up, you gotta let that go."

That's when Marv made his horrible mistake – he said: "Fuck that bitch, and that bitch-ass nigga." Off pure reaction, I pulled my hammer out and rocked up on ol' boy with a cold pistol whip. He dropped instantly, and I smacked his bitch-ass with the hammer a few more times.

"All right, Paper, he done," Dirt said, as he pulled me off him.

I looked at Marv and said: "You lucky I don't smoke yo' bitch-ass." Marv got up, leaking, and staggered out the door.

"I'ma end up smokin' this nigga," I said to Dirt.

"Naw, he don't want them problems, trust me," Dirt said.

"I hope not, 'cause I'ma end up givin' him more than he can handle."

"I already know, but he's gone, so just relax."

"Well, now I'ma go fuck his bitch," I said, smiling.

CHAPTER 11

I figured the whole situation had baby a little shook up, so I went to calm her down. I told her I didn't want to do all that, but bruh crossed the line when he called me a bitch. She nodded like she understood.

"Now that it's all over with," she said, pausing, "when I think about how you handled him, it turns me on." Then she started kissing me again, and my dick lifted right back up. I had all that aggression within me, it was time to take it out on her pussy.

I pulled baby into Dirt's bathroom, whipped out the pipe, and she started sucking. The head was incredible, but after a few minutes, I wanted to smash the pussy. She was ready for it, too, because as soon as I pulled her up, she dropped her panties. I put a condom on, bent her over the sink, and slid right in.

The pussy was wet, warm, and hella tight. While I was long-stroking baby from the back, I watched her make fuck faces through the mirror. I pounded her pussy for a solid five minutes before she started moaning so loud I couldn't even hold back any more. I busted a fat nut that had me shaking, while my thrusts got slower, but harder. Baby stopped moaning, I stopped pounding, and we locked eyes through the mirror.

I flushed the condom, washed my dick off in the sink real quick, then got dressed. Before we walked out, I said, "We ain't done yet. I'ma take you back to the spot and fuck you all night, like I promised."

She bit her bottom lip. "I can't wait," she said with a sexy-ass look.

We stepped out to Dirt's crazy-ass clapping and whistling. I guess they heard how I had baby in there moaning. I told bruh I'd catch him later, and we headed out.

We jumped in my whip, then I looked in my rear-view as I started the engine. For some reason, I couldn't see out my back window. I looked over my shoulder and couldn't believe it: my mu'fuckin' back window was busted out. Again! I already knew it was Marv's bitch ass. Who else could it have been?

I don't know if it was because I was drunk, or what, but I just started laughing. "See what yo' man did?" I said to Abby.

"Wow ... I can't believe he did that," she said.

I told her it was nothing, though, that I'd get a new one in the morning. Then we dipped to my house, with a busted-ass window.

As soon as we stepped in my room, we wasted no time getting to it. We fucked until the sun came up: this way, that way, and this way again. I told her I was gonna fuck her all night, and I meant it. Exhaustion eventually took over, and we both fell out.

I didn't wake back up until one in the afternoon. The only reason I did wake up was because baby woke me by sucking on my dick. "Oh, shit," I said, then baby really went to town. After busting a fat load in her mouth, she slurped everything up. *Damn, no wonder Marv was sprung on this*, I thought to myself.

I pulled my dick out her mouth, grabbed a rubber off my head board, then started hitting her doggy style. By the time I busted another nut, baby must've busted three. We were both sweating and out of breath. Baby was a loud one, too. I'm talking a real screamer. I was definitely feeling that.

All that fucking had me worn out, so I fired up a blunt and we relaxed. After about an hour we jumped in the shower. This is when I really noticed how sexy baby was with all her clothes off. While I was peeping her big-ass titties and fat ass, my dick reacted. once she seen it rocking up, she squatted down and started sucking.

After a couple minutes of enjoying her head game, I pulled out her mouth and slid in the pussy; this time raw, with no condom on. Her pussy was great with a condom on, so you can only imagine how it felt without one. I had her pinned up in the corner of the shower, sideways, with one leg up on the ledge of the tub. I had one hand playing with her clit in a fast motion while I slowly dicked her down. This had her screaming even louder than before. As soon as I got close to busting a nut, I pulled out, put it back in her mouth, and she finished me off.

CHAPTER 12

As time went, I kept fucking on Abby. I began picking her up after work each day, because she was cashing ya' boy out. She was a waitress at a restaurant called Carrol's, in Antioch, which is the next city over from the P. We weren't in a relationship or anything, we just had a good thing going.

Every time I picked her up from work, she'd hand me the tips she made that night. She usually made right around a hundred dollars in tips, so you know I needed that. I'd pick her up, get my dough, take her home, bash her guts, then I was gone.

Eventually, she earned her spot as my main bitch. I can recall the day vividly. I'd picked her up from work, and she didn't hand over her tips like usual. Instead she said, "I just got paid. Can you take me to cash my check?" I did, and when she came back out, she handed me every dollar!

I put the money in my pocket, and said: "So, I've upgraded from tips to the whole check, huh?"

She laughed, "I guess so."

I thanked her, and she rode around with me while I was busting knocks. My tank was on Egypt, so I pulled into the gas station. Before I could even get out the whip, she dug into her purse and handed me another twenty dollars, from her tip money.

Don't trip, I got it," I told her.

"No, put it in your tank."

"I ain't gonna deny ya' twice."

While pumping my gas, I thought, *I might have to make this bitch my main*. We had the conversation, and I asked her if she was ready to be my lady?

"Yes," she replied.

"What if you find out I'm fuckin' with other bitches; are you gonna trip and want to break up?"

"No. As long as I know you're mine, I'm not gonna trip."

That's what I wanted to hear. "OK, cool," I said, and we made it official.

Right after I told her we were official, she slid into the middle seat and reached for my zipper. I already knew what time it was, and my dick started to swell up. She pulled it out and put it in her mouth, and started bobbin'. It almost seemed like she was bobbing to the beat of the JT The Bigga Figga I had slumping. As she was bobbin', I made sure to hit every pot-hole on the road, on purpose! She sucked me so good we almost crashed – twice. We eventually made it to her spot, safely, and I dropped her off.

I was on my way to the freeway, stopped at a light, when I saw that nigga Marv coming out a liquor store. I grabbed my .40 Glock from under the seat and flipped a bitch. He must've recognized the whip, because bruh took off digging down the street.

CHAPTER 13

There was no way I was gonna let this sucka-ass nigga wiggle out of what he had coming. He probably thought he was running from an ass-whoopin'; but he'd soon find out I had other plans.

He turned down a street and I bent it sideways right behind him. Then he cut through a yard, and I knew the nigga was about to start hitting fences. I grabbed the hammer off my lap, an as soon as he went to hop a fence, I started busting.

Boom! Boom! Boom! Boom!

As he hit the top of the fence, he fell to the other side. Once I saw that, I knew I had to've tagged him. But about an hour later I got a call from Dirt. He told me Marv called him and told him I busted on him. That's when I knew I missed his lucky ass. Marv told Dirt to let me know he didn't want no smoke.

I laughed. I told Dirt to let Marv's scary-ass know it was on sight. "I'ma let him know," Dirt said, "but why you trippin' on this level?"

I never told Dirt that Marv had busted out my window, so I filled him in on the situation and let him know I wasn't playing. Last I heard about Marv, he moved out the P. Word was he moved in with his grandma in 'Frisco, started reppin' Fillmore and rapping under the name Messy Marv.

CHAPTER 14

1993 …

Me and Abby dragged our relationship along for a little over two years before I couldn't take it anymore. The bitch just got super-obsessive and jealous, like I didn't keep it real with her from the gate about me fucking with other bitches. But she caught feelings, and all that went out the window. The sex was always amazing, of course, but other than that, it was always an argument: Everywhere we went, "Why you lookin' at that bitch?" Every time I got off the phone, "Who was that?" Every time I came home, "Where you been? Who you been fuckin?"

I didn't have the time or patience for all that drama, my focus was on my paper. I did have feelings for her, which is why I put up with it for so long. But there was only so much I could take, so I ended up just cutting her off, and just did the single thing. It was better for me that way anyway. Don't get it twisted, though; I did still slide through and fuck her sexy ass from time to time. We basically just kept it a "friends with benefits" type of situation, which seemed to work!

$$$$$

The Seafood Festival was in town. If Pittsburg was famous for anything, it was definitely the Seafood Festival. People would travel from all over the U.S., even the world, to experience the exotic cuisine the Seafood Festival produced. You could get everything from clam chowder bread bowls to alligator and shark. Basically, if it comes from the sea, and you can eat it, you'll find it at the Seafood Festival.

Me and a few other Mob niggas had plans of going to the festival. We got fitted up in our best shit, and of course our jewels had us looking like we were from Alaska, we were so damn icy.

Every year we made it a thing to hit the Seafood Festival and knock new bitches, because not only did they come from far and wide, they also came in many different flavors. Now, I'm not talking about your average bitch from the hood, I'm talking about square rich bitches that deep down all have a thing for "Bad Boys." We were just as exotic as the seafood, and if a Bad Boy was a part of their fantasies, we were there to make their fantasies a reality.

And we didn't just knock one, Oh, no! We'd spend the whole day getting number after number. The ones from far away, we'd make plans to link up later that night. The ones from Cali, we'd hit them up when we felt like it, or it was convenient. We had a system where we'd put the name, and where she was from, right next to it. That way when we went out of town, we'd search our logs for any bitches from that city, and link up with them and their friends. It worked like a charm.

We were mobbin' through the festival standing out like a sore thumb amongst the crowd. Everywhere we looked, we had bitches breaking their necks. We also had some typical hating-ass niggas sending looks our way, of course, but we weren't worried about no haters. We stayed strapped up!

The thing about being a local, we knew how to get our weapons in past the security and metal detectors. The Seafood Festival is held downtown on the water, and there was a spot at the boat docks where the fence stopped at the water; we'd send one of the lil' niggas with a backpack holding our straps, and he'd hike along that fence until it ends, then he'd come right around it and into the Festival. It worked every time.

Anyway, we were doing our thing, poppin' at bitches and gettin' numbers, when I spotted this white girl. Now, she wasn't no regular-looking white girl; she was a thick bleach-blond, blue-eyed white girl, that looked like Pamela Anderson from Baywatch. She was so beautiful, she looked like an angel sent from God Himself.

As soon as I spotted her, she spotted me, and from a distance our eyes locked. It was as if we were magnetized to each other. We instantly made our way through the crowd towards one another as if we were friends.

CHAPTER 15

"Hey there, beautiful, I'm Paperboy," I greeted her, extending my hand.

"Hi, handsome, I'm Tiffany. Nice to meet you," she spoke, putting her hand in mine. I lifted it up to my lips and planed a little kiss on it. Which was something I'd always wanted to do, but hadn't met the one that inspired me to do it, until now.

"It's nice to meet you, as well," I grinned, flashing her a mouthful of diamonds. I seen it in her eyes that she was mesmerized by the sight. It was a trip how her sky-blue eyes reflected the twinkle of my diamonds like a mirror.

"So, tell me, Tiffany, where exactly do they make women so beautiful?" I asked.

"By that you mean, where am I from, right?" she giggled.

"Exactly, because you look like an angel sent from heaven."

"Oh, my God, you're so sweet." she blushed, lighting up like the sun. "I'm actually from Danville." she continued, referring to one of the richest cities in the Bay Area.

"Okay, Okay! So you're not that far away. Well, I'd definitely like to get to know you. Is it good to get your number?"

"Of course, it is! I'd definitely like to know you as well," she replied, flirtatiously.

I got her number, then noticed her look over her shoulder towards a small group of people that I figured was her friends: "Well, Tiffany, I'ma let you get back to enjoying your day. I'll call you soon, okay?"

"You better, I'll be waiting." She smiled as she walked off, shaking her ass with each stride, for me.

Usually I'd wait a few days, maybe even a few weeks, if I even call at all! But with Tiffany, I knew she was serious when she said she'd be waiting. So I said, 'fuck it' and hit her up that night.

"Hello?" she answered.

"Guess who?" I said, mischievously.

"Oh, my God, I was hoping you would call me tonight! Hi, Paperboy," she responded excitedly.

We conversated for about twenty minutes, getting to know each other a little bit, and I asked her if I could take her out to eat tomorrow. She said she had to go to the Sun Valley Mall in Concord, but after that she was free. So I told her I'd meet her there, and she could jump in with me and we'd go out to eat.

As planned, I met Tiffany at the Concord Mall, which is the next city over. When I arrived, she was already done shopping, and I met her at the entrance. She was standing there smiling as I walked up, and her beauty was breath-taking. I gave her a hug and the aroma of her perfume was pure sexiness.

"Do you like Mexican food?" I asked, hoping she did.

"I love Mexican food."

"Perfect, I know just the spot." And I did. There's an authentic Mexican restaurant in the P called "La Mecca," and it's known to be one of the best Mexican restaurants in the Bay Area.

We hit Highway 4 and as we were making our way into the P, my pager went off. I hit the Railroad exit and decided to stop and use the pay phone first, before we went to eat. I called the number, and it was some niggas in Antioch that needed some work: "Be out front in five minutes, I'm on my way!" I said as I hung up.

Me being about my paper and all, my money always comes first. Besides, baby was obviously interested in a thug, so she was going to get a lil' glimpse of the lifestyle as I went to do a transaction: "We're gonna have to take a lil' detour, I gotta get this money," I said nonchalantly.

"Oh, OK, that's fine," she responded, knowing I was talking about a drug deal.

I figured I might as well save the conversation for later, and I turned the music up. I couldn't help but smile when I looked over and seen baby nodding her head to the E-40 tape "Federal" I had slapping. "What you know about this?" I joked.

"Nothing," she admitted, "but I like the sound of it." She continued nodding to the beat.

"OK. I see you girl," I laughed.

I hit the Summersville exit in Antioch, bent a right and made my way to the Hudson Court Apartments.

Bruh was standing on the sidewalk, and I rolled up so my window was to the curb: "What's good, bruh, what you need?" Now, this was a nigga I'd done business with on multiple occasions, so it came as a bit of a surprise when he said: "Nigga, I need everything!" As he spoke, he lifted up his shirt revealing a .357 revolver tucked on his hip.

CHAPTER 16

Him just "showing" me his weapon and not actually pulling it out on me, was a mistake on his part. In this game, your first mistake is your worst mistake.

"It's good, bruh. I got you, you can have it," I said to make him think he had me spooked. I reached around with my left hand to grab the work, which blocked his view as my right hand slid under my shirt to the strap I had sitting on my lap. I always keep my thang on my lap, safety off, with one in the neck. The streets are a battlefield, so I gotta stay ready.

As I turned back around, the nigga had his eyes on the bundle. In a flash, I had my right hand out the window, and as soon as bruh seen the gun, shots rang out: "Boom … Boom! … Boom!"

As I was putting holes in the nigga, I seen a flash in my side mirror, and knew someone else was creeping up. But that nigga was also caught off guard by the shots, and he tried to run: "Boom! Boom! Boom!" I let that nigga have it, too, all in his back, and then I gassed off, tires screeching.

Before I could even gather my thoughts, I heard Tiffany screaming bloody murder.

"Fuck!" I yelled out loud, knowing the situation just got deeper.

Kaydah had given me some game a while back that fit this situation perfectly. He told me that if I ever had to feed a clip to some niggas, that after, I should hit the freeway and do a hundred miles an hour all the way to 'Frisco. By doing so, I could get there in record time, as long as I didn't attract the attention of highway patrol, of course. The goal was to get there and create an alibi by hitting a fast-food spot and being on camera, and then going to Pier 39. By saving all the receipts, I could prove I was in 'Frisco the day of the shooting. The fact is, it's basically impossible for me to have done the shooting, and then been eating at a Burger King in San Francisco 15 minutes later.

So that was the plan! I hit the freeway and quickly accelerated to a hundred plus. Tiffany began to calm down a bit as I was thinking about killing her. I didn't want to leave no witness. As she calmed down, I started talking to her: "Look, ma, they tried to rob me, I really had no choice," I spoke.

"I know you didn't, I've just never been through anything like that," she responded, as she wiped away her tears.

My mind was in overdrive as I drifted in and out of lanes through traffic. *Maybe she could be a part of my alibi*, I thought. Truth is, I really didn't want to kill the bitch, unless I had to. I just had to trust my gut on the situation.

"Look, this is what we're going to do; we're gonna go to 'Frisco and spend the rest of the day out there. If anybody ever asks, which they won't because nobody knows you're with me, but we were on a date in 'Frisco all day, OK?" I pitched to see how she would react.

She nodded, understanding what I was saying.

"Can I trust you to never mention this to anyone?" I asked.

"Yes, you can! I'll never tell a soul, trust me."

I believed her: "Well, I'ma need you to do me two favors."

"What's that?" she asked.

"First, fix your makeup. Then, when we hit the Bay Bridge, I'ma need you to throw this gun off the bridge into the water for me. Can you do that?"

"Yeah, I can do that," she agreed.

Before we hit the Bay Bridge, I broke the pistol down and put all the pieces into a paper bag. That way, when it hit the water, the paper bag would soften, and all the pieces would scatter as they sank. They'll never find the gun, believe that!

We hit the middle of the Bridge, and I slowed down so baby could toss the bag over. She launched it as far as she could and I hit the gas. Just as Kaydah said, I was walking into Burger King 15 minutes after the shooting, hand in hand with baby girl, and we were ordering Big Macs.

CHAPTER 17

I woke up the next day with one thing on my mind; I need another hammer! There wasn't any possibility I'd get caught slippin' without a thang on me. So I hit up Kaydah: "Bruh, I need to holla' at you. You at the hut?" I asked when he answered.

"Yeah, slide through," he responded.

"I'm on my way," I hung up.

I pulled up, knocked and he let me in: "What's the deal, bruh, is everything good?" he asked.

"I'm naked right now, bruh. Shit got ugly yesterday, so you already know I need a new thang," I stated without exposing any details.

He paused for a second, and I knew he was choosing his next words carefully. That's how he was. Always contemplating before he spoke. "Have you watched the news lately?" he asked.

"Naw, bruh, I haven't," I answered, wondering what the news was talking about.

"Well, just so you know, a couple niggas got bodied in Antioch yesterday. Be smooth out there," he warned. By me letting him know I ain't seen the news, he knew I don't know if the nigga survived or not. One thing he taught me from a young age, is to never speak on a shooting. Period! "Handle business, clean up, and leave it at that," he would say.

"It's all good, bruh, everything smooth," I stated.

"One-hunnid. I know someone that has a .40 cal on deck right now, and it comes with a stick," he let me know.

"Fo' sho', I want it!"

He hit the nigga up and let him know we were on our way. "Let's roll, we takin' my shit," he said, referring to his whip.

"Yeah, that's a good idea. It'll probably be best if I get a new whip also," I admitted.

"For sure, we'll hit up Fat Jim at the tow yard about a trade. You good wit' that?" he asked.

"You already know!" I replied.

Fat Jim owned a pick-n-pull tow yard in the P and was an easy 500 pounds. Hence the name, "Fat" Jim. He was about his business, though, and for a band, he crushed your car and you'd be driving away in something else, no questions asked. The thing is, you really can't be picky about what you drive off in. He'll give you a couple options, though, and they'll definitely run good. Guaranteed!

$$$$$

Over the years, Kaydah and I had grown real close. He looked at me like a son, and I looked at him like a pops. Since the very first time I had met him, I'd idolized him, and he ended up being the one that taught me everything I knew. A lot of what I'd learned was verbal, but some of the most important things I learned were nonverbal, because he always lead by example. So I learned to be observant and to pay close attention to my surroundings.

Kaydah was a man of many words and great wisdom, but he always paused and thought carefully before he spoke. He also made a lot of moves that weren't beneficial right away. "That's an investment. If the move shows promise to be beneficial in the future, it's worth investing in," he schooled me when I questioned one of his moves. That's what taught me to see the bigger picture and play the long game.

Even the streets considered me a mirror image of Kaydah. I would hear comments such as, "Boy, you's a fast-talking hustler, just like Kaydah," or "Look at you, nigga, fresh to death at all times, I know who you got that from." Even ones as simple as, "Yep! Like father, like son." But everything I learned from him, I took to heart, and those lessons made me wise beyond my years, and very dangerous. Needless to say, I was not one to be crossed.

CHAPTER 18

By the time we grabbed my new hammer, the tow yard was closed: "We'll handle that first thing in the mornin', my nigga'," Kaydah said.

"It's good!" I replied.

"In the meantime, we're gonna slide up to the city park and blow a blunt," he decided.

"Bet!"

We pulled into the back parking lot of the park and fired up. We were halfway through the blunt when I peeped some niggas gathering up for a dice game on the stage by the basketball court. "Look at them niggas. I should go break all their pockets," I said, half joking.

"Don't talk about it, be about it," Kaydah said, hypin' me up.

"You know what, that's exactly what I'ma do. You fucking' wit' it?" I asked Kaydah.

"Naw, I'm good, lil' nigga. But do yo' thing, break all them niggas," he replied.

"On the Mob. But do me a favor, and grab me a fifth of some Henny one time and bring it back for me?" I asked pulling out a big face.

"I got you, but I'm keeping the change" he said, snatching the hundred-dollar bill from my hand.

"On the Mob, I'ma need all mine," I laughed.

"I'll be right back," he said, as I bounced out and walked up to the dice game.

The dice game was in motion as I approached the huddle: "What's good? Is my money good over here?" I asked.

"All money's good over here. Why, you want in?" one of the niggas asked.

"Damn right I want in."

We introduced ourselves, and the game picked up where it left off. I was side-betting on a six-eight, when Kaydah pulled back up with my Hennessy. I lost that bet, and went to grab my bottle.

"Be smooth, lil' nigga. You know you don't be drinking like that," Kaydah warned.

"Don't trip, my nigga. I'll be smooth. Besides, you know I got my .40 thang on me," I responded.

"Exactly! Don't get all drunk and do some stupid shit," he said, talking shit as he started to pull off.

"I won't. Where my change at, nigga?" I asked as he was rolling away.

"That's me, like I told you!" he barked as he gassed off.

I pulled back up on the dice game, yanked the bottle out of the brown paper bag, and seen my change at the bottom. I just shook my head as I put it in my pocket, and I squatted back down. Then I popped by bottle and took a swig.

There was seven of us all together, so the side-bets were poppin'. I was strictly side-betting for a while as I was feeling out their game. Finally, I declared my back-fade and was waiting for the next niggas to crap out. In the meantime, I was sipping on my bottle.

Bruh on dice finally crapped out, and a new nigga was in; I was next, so I challenged him: "Dub you don't?" I said, upping the stakes with a nonchalant swagger. Them niggas were shooting ones and fives. I was already starting to feel myself off the Henny.

"I do, the nigga accepted confidently, as he dropped four five-dollar bills next to my twenty. He hit a seven out of the gate: "Forty you don't," I said, raising the stakes even more.

"I do!" he said, leaving the money he won on the ground. He rolled a four.

"He don't ten-four for dub," I said, challenging a side-bet.

"He do!" one nigga accepted.

Two rolls later, the nigga crapped out and I was on dice, up forty dollars: "Dub I hit?" I challenged my new opponent.

"You don't," he accepted.

I hit the bottle, schooled the dice, and rolled them out the tip of my fingers: "Hit, dice," I demanded as I double-snapped my fingers. Eleven out the gate. I hit!

"Bet back," my opp declared, dropping another twenty dollars.

I got on a hot streak and most of the niggas were betting with me. They were celebrating as they collected their winnings every time I hit. Then they anxiously awaited my next roll. I was hitting point after point. My stroke was on; I held the dice for a solid ten minutes before I crapped out, which is almost impossible to do in a crap game.

Once I got back on dice, I got right back in rhythm. Next thing I knew, niggas were fallin' off left and right: "I'm tapped …"; "That's a wrap! …"; "I'm out …" It took me no longer than forty-five minutes to break the whole dice game. Niggas took their "L's" like champs, though, and we parted ways.

By that time, I was already faded. Once I started walking back to the Lo, it really hit me! My eyesight was low key blurry, and shit was starting to spin. But I kept pushing. My drunk ass was walking with the almost-empty bottle all out in the open, like it was good. Doing so, I ended up catching the attention of a pig rolling by.

CHAPTER 19

I didn't even see the pig. Next thing I knew, two of them rolled up on me and hopped out with guns drawn: "Drop the bottle and put your hands up," one demanded.

I put one hand up and hit the bottle one last time, killing it before I tossed it. Then, I put my other hand up. It was at that moment I remembered I had the .40 with a stick on me. But I had nowhere to go, and their guns were already drawn on me.

One of the pigs cuffed me, and asked: "Do you have anything on you?"

"Nope," I lied.

He started patting me down and felt the weapon on my hip: "I thought you didn't have anything on you?" he asked, as he removed it and handed it to his partner.

"What I look like tellin' on myself?" I answered with a slur.

He didn't even respond, just finished emptying my pockets of all the different crumpled and wadded up bills. They were in every single pocket, even some in my sock. Then, the pig put me in the back of his squad car, and I threw up all over it.

I was on my way to the County.

$$$$$

I ended up getting sentenced to six months since it was my first time ever being arrested. After sentencing, I was transferred to West County Jail in Richmond, California, to serve my sentence. I stepped off the bus and entered the receiving and releasing Unit with about ten other niggas, varying in age and crimes, along with time. We were all lined up in front of a thick yellow line painted on the floor. No one spoke, but I could tell who was with the shit, and who was scary, just by their demeanors.

A sliding metal door clanked open, and a giant of a correctional staff member stepped through it. He had to've stood a towering 6'6", weighing at least a solid 260 pounds.

"All right, y'all. How you came into this world, is how you're leaving it. Strip!" he demanded.

Most of the niggas in the line were used to the ritual already, but I was new to the bullshit. I stripped down ass-hole naked, and was feeling hella awkward with a bunch of naked niggas all around me. I was outfitted in my "prison" clothes, and sent to my unit to serve my six months.

When I entered, I saw niggas sitting in the day room watching TV and slapping bones on one side, while others were hitting free weights on the opposite side. Once I seen the weights, I knew that's where I would be spending most of my time. I peeped a few familiar faces, some happy to see me, and others not so much. But I wasn't tripping, I had planned on putting down a demo anyway; now I had a couple targets.

This being my first time locked up and all, I stepped in aggressive, with a chip on my shoulder. Matter of fact, I wasn't there five minutes, and I was already rushing my first target.

Once the nigga saw me coming, he knew what time it was. He stood right up and began to say something, but he never got it out his mouth. I caught the nigga with a solid right to his snot-box, and his shit instantly started leaking, but he wasn't going out like no sucka'.

Everybody spread out as the nigga stepped back and squared up with me: "Nigga, I've been needin' a good fade. We finna' lock like some pits," he proclaimed as he stepped forward ready to chunk 'em.

He threw two quick punches: I ducked one, but was somewhat dazed by the second. The nigga seen that and tried to follow up with a right hook that I side-stepped, as I fired off a combo of my own. My left and right was vicious as it caught the nigga in the mouth and eye, doing damage.

The fight was the center of attention. With adrenalin pumping, niggas were standing on top of chairs and tables, not wanting to miss the action. They were cheering and hollering, as we fought a bloody draw. In the end, I was lumped up a lot more than I would've liked, but my point was well received.

I was definitely ready for the thunder dorm.

CHAPTER 20

I knocked down my six months with ease, got out, and went straight to the block. It felt good stepping back into my hood, and the streets themselves seemed to welcome me home; the sound of whips slapping, the Bay-Bay's Kids running around laughing, and the lovely stench of bomb-ass-weed mingled in the air as I took it all in.

I needed a blunt myself, and I knew Kendra was smoking one at that very moment, so I headed towards her crib.

"What's up wit' it, my nigga?" Kendra yelled as I bent the block. "I've been waitin' fo' yo' stupid-ass to get home," she said, giving me dap and pulling me into a thug embrace; we gave each other's back a quick fist pound.

"On some real shit, the block's been missin' you out here," she expressed, as I was peepin' the blunt in her ear.

"Bitch, what you waitin' for? Fire that blunt up!" I demanded, as I started laughing because she hated when I called her "bitch."

"Nigga, fuck you!" she playfully barked, as she sparked up the blunt and passed it.

I hit that mu'fucka' like I'd been blowing every day, and instantly coughed up a lung.

"Yeah, nigga! That's that fire fo' yo' virgin lungs. Quit playin' and pass that shit," she clowned.

"What's been poppin' wit' you, though?" I asked, as she damn near smoked half the blunt in one hit.

"Shit, just clockin' these dolla's. But look at you, though, nigga," she spoke, admiring the difference six months had made: "You done got taller, and you're on swole. You must've stayed working out," she acknowledged.

"You betta' believe I did! Shit, wasn't nothin' better to do," I bragged, as I flexed on her.

"If you don't knock it off," she laughed as she passed me back the blunt, which was more like a doobie now. I could tell she missed a nigga and was glad I was back home." I got a lil' surprise fo' you, my nigga," she blurted out with a twinkle in her eye and a devilish grin.

"What is it? Some pussy?" I cracked.

"No, nigga, it ain't no pussy. It's better than that," she retorted.

"Better than a nut after six months?" I asked as if to say "No Way!"

"Better! Just come on!" she said, as she darted off towards her spot.

We stepped in, and she told me to grab a seat. I plopped down onto the leather sofa with the plastic still on it, while she vanished off into her room. "Close yo' eyes, nigga," she yelled out at me.

You got me fucked up. I ain't closin' my eyes," I spat, wondering what type of surprise she had in store for me.

"Nigga, quit playin' and just close your eyes," she begged.

"All right! They're closed." I gave in with a grin while I squinted so I could peek. I seen her put something on the coffee table in front of me, but wasn't able to make out what it was.

"Okay, open 'em up," she encouraged eagerly.

I looked down at a Q.P. of some coke and a brand new nickel-plated .40 Glock with an extended clip. Kendra was right; it was definitely better than some pussy. She knew it, because she knew I kept it Money Over Bitches: "Just a lil' somethin' to get you back on yo' feet," she said, smiling proudly, "and you know we can't have you out here naked, ya' dig?"

I didn't speak as I let the gesture sink in a bit.

"I got somethin' else for you, too," she said dryly, trying to keep a straight face; but failing miserably.

"What?" I asked, full of curiosity.

"Follow me, I'll show you," she said, leading the way down her hallway. I followed and she stopped in front of her spare bedroom. Then she swung the door open.

My eyes widened, and my jaw dropped a bit, as I seen a sexy-ass light-bright bitch sprawled out on the bed butt-booty-naked, in a seductive pose.

"Business before pleasure, my nigga! This is Star. Star, this is Paperboy," she said, making the informal introduction.

My dick was already hard from my scan of Star's assets; she had lustrous long black hair, big round tits with pepperoni-sized nipples, a slim stomach, and a pretty Brazilian-waxed pussy. I had an obvious tent pitched in my pants, and Star was looking right at it. As she licked her full lips that were made for giving blow jobs, she spread her legs wide open, inviting me in.

I bit my lower lip, ready to beat that pussy up.

"Make sure you save me some!" Kendra joked, pushing me into the bedroom and closing the door.

CHAPTER 21

I woke up the next morning at about 5:30 a.m. I was lying on my back with both hands behind my head, looking at the ceiling. Star was curled up beside me hogging all the covers. I was in deep thought as the cool soothing air conditioning breezed over my bare body. The powerful release of six months had come and went several times during the course of the night. And like a nigga with a ravishing hunger who eats until he's full, I was definitely satisfied.

Just as Kendra had observed, I'd grown taller and my body as well as my feet were bigger. My clothes and shoes didn't even fit me no more, I needed a whole new wardrobe. So, I decided that after I went to see Kaydah, I'd stop by my spot in Parkside and dig into what little money I had left (I'd used practically all my savings and paid cash for a three-bedroom house a few months before I'd gotten arrested), and I'd go buy myself some new gear.

When I left, Kendra and Star were still sleeping. It was only 6 a.m., but Kaydah was an early-bird like myself, so I knew he'd be up. I stepped to his door and knocked on it.

Knock! Knock! Knock!

"Who's that?" Kaydah asked.

"It's Paper, bruh."

"My nigga!" he said, as he swung the door open: "Come in, bruh, I was just 'bout to fire up this blunt," he continued, holding up a blunt that had at least a half-an-eighth stuffed in it.

"Fo' sho', fire that bitch up," I said, locking the door behind me.

He sparked the blunt, passed it to me, and turned on Mac Dre's "Young Black Brotha," an album he'd recently released from the Fresno County jail. I'd heard about it, but this was the first time I'd actually got to hear it. We were both noddin' our heads to Dre's unique flow, as we passed the blunt back and forth.

After we killed the blunt, the good weed had me spaced out like the solar system. Then, something landed in my lap and brought me back to reality. I looked down and seen some car keys: "Welcome home, my nigga," Kay said with a smirk.

"What these go to, bruh" I asked, hoping it was something dope.

"You got locked up before we could trade yo' whip in to Fat Jim, so I decided to surprise you wit' something clean when you got home. Come on, it's outside," he said, rising to his feet and heading for the door.

We walked outside and he pointed: "That's you, right there," he said, pointing to an all-white '68 Cougar.

I couldn't believe my eyes; I'd always wanted one, and even remembered telling Kaydah that I wanted to get one. I was speechless!

"Let's take it fo' a test drive," he suggested.

I just nodded and started walking towards it, still speechless.

"Hold on, let me grab some trees and lock up," Kaydah said, as he headed back inside real quick.

I got in the Coug-nut and turned the ignition over. The engine fired right up and rumbled like an empty stomach. I hit the gas hard a couple times, and the engine roared like a grizzly, then returned to its rumble.

Kaydah jumped in and I put it in drive without even letting it warm up, then I gassed off leaving a parallel trail of rubber and smoke behind me. It was definitely fast, and I was in love as I maneuvered its power through the streets. I looked over and saw Kaydah was breaking down some trees in a hundred-dollar bill: "We need a blunt," he informed me.

We were around the corner from my spot, so I decided to hit the quick stop. I grabbed the blunt and decided to hit a left on Bruno, drove past my spot, took a right on 17th and another left on Davi.

As we rolled down the block, Kaydah was putting the finishing touches on the blunt, and something caught my eye.

"Aye, Kaydah, peep this shit, my nigga."

CHAPTER 22

There was a circle of Bay-Bay's Kids in the middle of the street. At first I thought it was some lil' nigga's finna get down real quick. But as we got closer, I seen a lil' ghetto white boy, maybe 10 years old, and he was Putting boxing gloves on a lil' white girl maybe 8 years old. I assumed she was the white boy's lil' sis'. On the other side, a lil' black nigga about the same age as the white girl, was also putting on some boxing gloves. The rest of the kids were spectators.

"Pull over, nigga, let's watch this shit," Kaydah demanded. I did, and he fired up the blunt for the show.

The white boy spoke: "Yeah, you was talkin' that shit. I told you I'll make my lil' sister come out here and scrape yo' lil' ass."

"Hakeem! You bett' not let that white girl scrape you," one of the spectators yelled form the crowd.

"What? I'm finna knock her ass out," the lil' nigga they called Hakeem yelled back.

I was looking at the white girl as she got ready to fight a boy, and I seen zero fear in her; in fact, I seen nothing but confidence. The white boy also had nothing but confidence in his lil' sister: "Kaydah, I got a hundred dollas sayin' the white girl scrapes the lil' nigga?" I proposed.

"What? Nigga, that's easy money. Of course I'm takin' that bet," Kaydah accepted.

"Scrape that nigga, Gabby," the white boy yelled, and the white girl rushed up on the lil' nigga. They started swinging and were connecting with each other, blow for blow. Then the white girl swung a smooth haymaker and caught the lil' nigga square on his chin. He dropped instantly!

"Ooooohhhh," everyone said in unison, including myself and Kaydah.

"Nigga, you betta' get yo' ass back up," one of the spectators yelled. But the lil' nigga was dazed and didn't want any more issues. "I said get yo' ass back up," the same spectator said, as he pushed in from the crowd and swooped the lil' nigga up off his ass.

The lil' white girl jumped right back into her stance, ready to fight. But the lil' nigga just shook his head, "No." At that, the same spectator started pulling his gloves off, and then kicked him right in his ass: "Get yo' scary ass in the house, nigga. I can't believe you let that white girl whip yo' ass," he spat, as the lil' nigga just took off running.

"Aahhh, ha, ha, ha …" I erupted in laughter: "Pay up, nigga," I told Kaydah.

Even he was hot the lil' nigga got whipped by the white girl. Especially because he lost a hundred. He just shook his head and tore mine off. I slid my big-Ben in my pocket and started the whip. "Let's roll, nigga," I said, between puffs on the blunt.

"What made you take the white girl?" Kaydah asked as I passed him the blunt.

"Her confidence and her demeanor. I looked into her eyes and I seen no fear," I admitted. "You're the one who told me it's the quiet confident ones you gotta watch out for," I reminded him, with a smirk.

"That is true. She sure did flat-back that lil' nigga, though," Kaydah said, as he, too, started laughing.

We pulled up in front of his spot: "Bruh, I gotta go snatch up some new clothes. I'll catch up with you later. And good looking out on the whip, big bruh, fo' real!" I said, thanking him.

"Yo' ass did blow up overnight. The size looks good on you, but that 'fro don't," he laughed, and then reached into his pocket, pulling out some dough, "here's a stack on some fits, and you're welcome," he continued, handing me a band.

"Good lookin' bruh. And don't be talking 'bout my 'fro, I'ma 'bout to get my shit twisted," I said, as I patted my 'fro with both hands.

"Handle that! I got another surprise for you also, come by later, around three," he said, all serious.

"What is it?" I asked.

"Just slide back through at 3, 3:30," he said, as he walked off.

CHAPTER 23

I pulled up to the fit spot to grab some T's, some kicks, and some snap-backs to match. One thing's for sure when it comes to my gear; the hats always have to match the kicks. I parked and hopped out.

As I was walking through the parking lot towards the entrance, I peeped a sexy-ass five-foot-nothing Asian female walking out the check cashing right in front of me. Being the Mac that I am, I automatically started poppin': "Hey, there, beautiful," I smiled as I looked into her barely visible, but still noticeably pretty brown eyes.

"Oh, hello," she responded, obviously caught off guard.

"I didn't mean to startle you, I just couldn't help but notice how beautiful you are, and I wanted you to know that," I complimented, as I was admiring her perfect thickness.

"Wow! That's really sweet, thank you," she beamed, flashing a pearly white smile that belonged on a Colgate commercial. At that moment I realized she'd walked right up to a ruby-red Bens on chrome rims.

"You're welcome, beautiful, have a great day," I winked as I started walking off.

"I will, sweety, you do the same."

With that, I walked into the fit shop to snatch up whatever grabbed my attention. Mind you, the sexy Asian female was in her late 30s or early 40s, and I was only 20, so I was just being a flirt, and enjoying the exchange of words. But she sure did seem to enjoy watching my eyes travel her body from head to toe as I was eye-fucking her.

After I grabbed a solid week's worth of fits, I cashed out and made my way out the shop. To my surprise, the ruby-red Benz was still parked in the same spot. As I looked with what I'm sure was "amazement" on my face, the slightly tinted driver window began to slide down; once again, she revealed her bright smile, making it obvious she'd waited for me.

"Damn, beautiful, if I'd known you'd be waiting on me, I wouldn't have taken so long," I laughed, returning a smile of my own.

"I know, what were you doing? Buying up the whole store?," she joked, looking at the numerous bags I had dangling from each arm.

"Shit, somethin' like that," I responded as I shrugged my shoulders.

"Well, honestly, I waited because I didn't think I'd ever get to see you again if I didn't," she confessed shyly.

"I'm definitely glad you did," I said, as I made my way towards her. "I never thought I'd see you again, either. I'm Paperboy." I continued, reaching my hand out and slightly into her window.

"I'm Joyce, nice to meet you," she uttered, as she put her tiny manicured hand in my hand.

"I don't want to hold you up any longer than I already have, so why don't we swap numbers, and I'll hit you up later, so we can get to know each other better," I suggested, as I let the handshake linger a second.

"I'd love that," she responded with a seductive tone.

We traded numbers, and she continued: "Well, if you're not busy, maybe we can hang out tonight? I'ma be home all by myself anyway, and I'd much rather spend my night getting to know you," she continued in her seductive tone, as she slightly bit her bottom lip.

I can't even front, I was already getting turned on as I started to imagine how the night might unfold.

"I'm all yours tonight, baby," I answered confidently, looking deep into her eyes. "What time should I come through?" I asked, still locked into her eyes like we were having a staring contest.

"Perfect! I'll call you around six with the directions," she answered, matching my stare.

"I'll be ready! See you soon, sexy," I said, as I started off towards my new whip.

Damn, this day just keeps gettin' better and better, I thought, as I seen Joyce looking to see what car I was getting into. I tossed my new gear in the back seat, and got in. Joyce waved as she drove off, smiling again.

CHAPTER 24

It was barely noon, so I had plenty of time until Joyce would be calling with directions to her spot. My baby afro was perfectly picked out, but I wanted to get my shit twisted, and I knew just the person. A crackhead we called "Tee Tee" used to own her own hair solon, and she was the best in the whole P when it came to braids. She'd do designs, put your name, or anything else you wanted, and she' do it for a nickel-rock. So, I decided to go home, carve her a nickel, shower, fit up, and then go see Tee Tee.

Talk about carvin' a rock; my skills were still on point, as I carved it with the skills of a sculptor. I went ahead and busted down a handful, just to have them on deck.

After I got out the shower, I had to figure out exactly what I wanted to wear; I decided to keep it simple, and went with the coke-white Jordans and a white T, with some black Tommy Hilfiger jeans. It was only one-thirty, so I decided to go get twisted, and then I'd go see what this other surprise was that

Kaydah was talking about. Besides, Kaydah was right around the corner from Tee Tee's anyway.

By the time I was done getting twisted, it was almost three. "Perfect timing, let's go see what Kaydah's got going on," I said out loud to myself.

$$$$$

"A lot has changed while you were away, my nigga," Kaydah said, as I followed him into his spot. We walked in and I saw a lil' baby boy that couldn't be more than a few months old. "Meet your nephew, Ivan, Jr.," he continued, shocking the hell out of me.

"What? My nephew?" I asked, confused.

"This is my son, Paperboy," he responded.

To say I was dumbfounded would be an understatement: "What …? When …? How …? I was only gone six months!" I managed to utter.

"Remember that bitch Quanisha I be fucking with from time to time?" he asked, referring to some hood-rat.

"Yeah! You and everyone else!" I said, being a smart-ass.

"Yeah, her!" he laughed, shaking his head, "Well, the bitch popped up on me nine-months pregnant, looking like a blimp, talking about the baby is mine."

"And, what, you believed her?" I asked, knowing better.

"Hell, naw, nigga. You already know I denied that. Especially because I never hit wit'out a glove on," he said, pausing, and then he took a deep breath: "Bruh, the bitch had the lil' nigga and took my

77

mu'fuckin' ass to Jerry Springer! Long story short; the baby came back mine, bruh," Kaydah said, smiling.

"Damn, bruh! That's crazy as fuck," was all I could say.

"Tell me about it! The whole damn P was watching the episode, and was laughin' they asses off when my jaw hit the floor," he said, laughing hisself, "Niggas still be yellin': 'Jerry! Jerry! Jerry!' from time to time when they see me." As soon as he said that, I couldn't help but laugh so hard my stomach hurt.

"But you already know. He's mine, so I'ma step up. There ain't no way I'm finna leave my lil' nigga wit' that hood-rat ass bitch!" he said, keeping it all the way real.

"On the Mob, I wouldn't either," I agreed. "Well, quit playin' and let me hold my nephew, nigga," I barked, putting my mean-mug on. Kaydah just laughed and handed me his spitting image in the form of a shitty-diapered, snot-nosed, lil' nappy-headed baby.

Kaydah swore the bitch pulled an okey-doke on him and poked a hole in the condom. Wouldn't surprise me, though; them gold-digging bitches will fuck around and drown, they're so damn thirsty. He refused to have anything to do with her, and instead of paying child support and allowing her to raise his son, he took her busted-down broke ass to family court and got full custody of his lil' man. That lil' boy was Kaydah's pride and joy, the heir to his empire. The only time he let his hood-rat baby mamma see the lil' nigga was when he needed a babysitter.

CHAPTER 25

It was 6:00 on the dot, and I was parked in front of Kaydah's, waiting for Joyce to call with directions. I was twisting up a blunt, making sure I rolled it perfectly; not too tight, not too loose, and definitely not pregnant. I flicked my Bic lighter and sparkled up the bat I'd just rolled. I concentrated on the yellow-blue flame as it sucked into the tip of the blunt, creating an orange glow. I inhaled deeply, threw my head back, and blew a stream of smoke into the air, filling up the car with my favorite smell.

I blew half the blunt and was just putting it out when my phone rang:

Ring! Ring! Ring!

"It's about time," I joked, without even asking who it was first.

"What you talkin' 'bout, my nigga?" Kendra asked.

"Oh, shit, my bad. I was expecting a call from someone. What's good, though?"

"Bruh, you got this bitch Star over here all sprung and shit. She ain't stopped talking 'bout you yet," she explained.

"Is that right?" I asked, not really caring.

"Yeah, she said you fucked her like you was fresh out of jail. Then she said: 'Oh, wait, he was fresh out.' And we started laughing so hard, we cried tears," Kendra said, laughing again.

"You bitches probably hella high, but I fo' sho' gave her that fresh out, dope dick," I bragged.

"Well, she wanted me to let you know she's ready for the encore," she said, relaying the message.

"I have plans tonight, but slide me her number, and let her know I'll hit her up soon."

Kendra gave me Star's number, I logged it into my contacts, and hung up. By now, it was past 6:30, and still no call from Joyce! *She's probably taking hella long to get ready*, I thought, because females always take forever to get ready. And Joyce's sexy-ass absolutely fit that profile.

I wasn't going to wait on her all night, though, and if she flaked, well, then Star would get that 'encore' after all. With that in mind, I started the engine and gassed off. I turned on Some 2PAC, cranked the volume all the way up, and started pulling up on baseheads to make some sales and spread the word that I was home. Next thing I knew, my phone was ringing again.

I pushed pause on my tape deck and answered; it was, in fact, Joyce.

"So you decided to call after all?" I asked, guessing she was hesitant.

"Yeah, I'm not going to lie, I got ready and was super excited. But then I got nervous and started to chicken out," she replied honestly.

"So, you were going to flake on me, huh? Well, what made you change your mind?" I asked out of curiosity.

"A couple shots of vodka," she admitted with a giggle.

I laughed myself, "OK, OK. At least you're honest. I have to say that I'm glad you called, though," I expressed.

"Me, too. I'm ready for us to start getting to know each other," she said, in that sexy tone of hers.

"Are you sure?" I asked firmly.

"Absolutely"; she sounded confident.

"Absolute like that vodka, huh?" I asked, half joking, while referring to the popular brand of vodka.

"Oh my god! How did you know," she giggled, sounding a little buzzed.

"Let's just call it a wild guess," I said, feeling cocky that I guessed right.

She gave me her address, which I recognized as a nicer part of Antioch called "Deer Valley."

"I'm on my way. Give me 15 minutes," I said, looking forward to seeing her again.

"OK, sweety, I'll see you soon."

CHAPTER 26

I pulled up to a nice two-story house in the middle of the block. It wasn't the nicest house on the block, but it was nice, and it fit right in with the ones surrounding it. I decided to park a few houses down and in the street, rather than in the driveway next to her Benz.

I grabbed some condoms out of my glove box, and my pistol, then I got out; better safe than sorry. I locked up my whip and dialed Joyce as I approached her house.

She picked up after the second ring: "You're here?" she asked.

"Yep, I'm walking up to your door now," I said, and the door opened on cue.

She was standing there looking sexy and elegant at the same time, and our eyes locked. They seemed to be stuck to each other. I admired how her pearly white teeth composed the perfect smile, and I admired how her cosmetics were applied just right; not too much, but enough to highlight her beauty. I couldn't help but be intrigued by her.

"Come in," she said, moving to the side, giving me a narrow path to enter.

As I walked past her, I smelled her sweet-scented perfume. She closed the door, and I watched her ass-cheeks shift as she led me to the spacious living room. As I stepped in, I was greeted by the sound of the Warrior Game playing on her T.V.

"Can I get you anything?" She asked politely.

"Absolute'ly," I laughed, as I played off the joke I'd made earlier.

"Coming right up," she giggled, shaking her head as if to say: "You're too much."

I took a seat and sunk into the large, comfortable sofa. Once she was out of sight, I removed my hammer and tucked it under the sofa cushion. A minute later, she returned with the bottle and two glasses with ice. She set them both on table coasters and splashed each one until the alcohol leveled with the ice. Then she handed me mine.

"Good lookin' out, sexy," I said, in a low tone, as I took in her feminine essence again, and allowed my eyes to scan her body. She wore a short mocha-colored wrap dress that stopped right under her derriere. It fit snugly around her small but thick frame, revealing one shoulder and her toned upper back. Her thighs and fit legs glistened as if just lotioned.

"You look very sexy," I said, interrupting the silence and putting emphasis on the word "very."

"Thank you! You're looking handsome, yourself." She blushed as she took a seat diagonally to my right on the love-seat. She leaned over into the couch and crossed her legs to get comfortable. As she did, I couldn't help but notice she wasn't wearing any panties. My manhood throbbed at the sight, and I licked my lips as I looked up and seen her watching me with delight.

The lust and passion that burned in her eyes signaled what time it was. She lifted one finger to her mouth, and I watched intently as she sucked on it erotically and spread her legs giving me a perfect view of the prettiest pussy I've ever seen.

She looked into my eyes as she took the moisture from her mouth and began to circle it on her clitoris. At that moment, all the blood rushed to my pole, swelling it up to the point it badly needed to escape the confines of my pants.

I felt my body heating up, so I took off my shirt, revealing my muscle-toned body. Then, I loosened my pants and let them, as well as my boxers, fall to the floor. I grabbed my thick hard cock and began to stroke it as I watched Joyce pleasure herself.

"You like what you see?" she asked, as she inserted two fingers inside herself. Her pussy was soaking wet, and she started grinding her hips to her own beat as she fingered her twat.

My swollen cock was urging to get in the game, but I contained myself, trying to savor the moment, not wanting to be too eager. Instead I moved next to her on the love-seat and slid my own fingers inside of her melted pot of honey. Then, I slid the single strap off her shoulder and pulled the top of her dress down, exposing two perfectly ripe melon-size titties.

I started sucking on her nipples, tugging on them gently with my lips and teeth. As I did so, I lifted one of her legs into the air and positioned myself so I could rub her clit with the tip of my dick. I could feel the sizzling from her coochie as I teased her.

"I want to feel you inside me," she whispered, as she wrapped her arms around my back.

CHAPTER 27

I stood up, grabbed a condom out of my pocket and put it on. I positioned her in the doggy-style position over the arm rest of the love-seat, and slid right in that tiny wet Asian pussy. I was diving deep into her with a slow-paced long stroke. My thick hardness was throbbing inside her as her walls contracted around my large shaft.

"Damn, you got some good pussy," I said, as I rocked in and out of her with a slow, passionate rhythm. She was definitely deprived of a good fuck, because she was tighter than a virgin and screaming with delight.

She threw her wide-ass back and matched my strokes, pump for pump, as I gripped her love handles, allowing me to dig even deeper.

"Ohh, fuck me!" she cried out in ecstasy, as my length reached depths she didn't even know existed: "Ohh! Yes! Just like that, daddy," she continued as I sped up and pounded a little harder.

I started to grunt as I continued to bash her walls in, feeling my nut build up to the point of exploding.

"Make me cum daddy! Make me cum!" she begged.

"I'ma make you cum, baby! Daddy's dick is definitely gonna make you cum." I continued pounding, never breaking my stride.

"Oh … ! Fuck … ! Me …! Daddy …! I'm! Cumming!" she screamed between collisions as her body tensed from the intensity of her orgasm.

I felt her body convulsing from her orgasm; "Oh! Shit!" I said, as I busted a nut so fat that the condom busted; revealing a wetness that kept me cumming for an extra few seconds.

We lay in silence for a while, just trying to catch our breath, as we comprehended the mind-blowing experience we'd just enjoyed.

"The condom busted, didn't it?" Joyce asked, breaking the silence.

"Yeah! That it did!" I answered not exactly sure what to say.

"I literally felt you explode inside me," she said, biting her bottom lip as if the thought turned her on.

"So what are you going to do? I know you don't want to get pregnant," I asked, hoping I was right.

"It's all good, I'll have my friend bring me a morning-after pill in the morning," she answered.

Joyce looked tired, and I felt my eyes getting heavy as well. So I picked Joyce up and carried her as she directed me to her room. Then we just lay there in silence, until we both passed out.

The next morning I woke up to Joyce staring at me.

"Good morning"; I smiled as visions of last night flashed in my mind.

"I want you to know that I have a man, and I usually wouldn't do something like this, but he's locked up, and I've been lonely and horny as fuck," she admitted, getting it off her chest.

"Calm down. It's OK. I understand and don't mind keeping you company from time to time until he gets out," I replied, and she just continued looking at me in silence. "How long until he gets out?" I continued.

"Two years!" she said it like it was forever.

"I definitely respect you holdin' yo' man down like that. Two years will fly by, but in the meantime, I'ma enjoy the time we'll have together," I confessed as I pulled her to me and started kissing her.

"I ... bet ... you ... will" she managed to say between kisses and then she started kissing her way down my bare chest and stomach, until she reached my already hard cock; taking it deep into her throat as she started sucking away.

"Oooo shit," I whispered, as I laid my head back down on the pillow, enjoying her tongue and throat action.

Then her phone started ringing. She grabbed it and gave me the "Shhh" sign, putting her finger to her lips: "Hello, babe," she spoke, and then she started sucking my dick again: "I miss you, too, my love." Suck ... Suck ... Suck ...

Fifteen minutes later, their conversation was over and she was swallowing all my kids.

"So, what's for breakfast?" I asked, smiling.

"It's a surprise," she smirked, as she got up to go cook me something.

CHAPTER 28

As she walked out of the room towards the kitchen, I couldn't help but admire her sexiness. Although, she was just a tiny thing, she definitely had a nice full body with curves in all the right places. She must've felt my eyes on her, because she shook that booty like it was made of jello.

After a few minutes, I walked into the living room and sat in a chair that gave me a clear view of the kitchen, Joyce in particular. As she cooked for me butt-ass naked, she was slowly maneuvering her heart-shaped ass side to side while she enjoyed the sounds of Keith Sweat's "You Got Me Twisted." It made me smile, because baby had no idea I was there watching, and she was jamming to the tunes.

She had me in a trance. As I watched intently, my pipe started reacting to the show. Like a magnet to some metal, I was on my way. I stepped into the kitchen and swiftly slid up on her: "Hey, sexy, you got it smellin' good up in here. What's on the menu?" I asked, as I wrapped my arms around her stomach and pressed my hardness against her perfect bubble-butt.

"Just an Asian dish my momma taught me. You're going to love it," she said, as she continued to dance, slowly grinding her cakes against my erect cock.

"I'm sure I will," I said, as I was watching her hips, so that my dick was right between her buns like a hot dog.

She reached behind, grabbed my muscle with her little hand, leaned forward and slid me right into her wetness. Feeling me pressed against her must've turned her on, because her insides were warm and extremely juicy.

"You never cease to amaze me," I spoke into her ear as I was slowly piping her down.

Next thing I knew, she turned off the burner and moved the pan over to a cool spot on the stove.

I turned her around, picked her up and I carried her over to the table, sitting her on it. Then I laid her back on it and lifted her legs up to my chest. Her ass was on the edge of the table, and my dick lined right up with her pussy. I slid in and stood there beatin' it up. I had her legs spread apart with each hand gripping an ankle. Doing so gave me an amazing view; I was sliding in and out of her, and watching her titties bounce with each stroke, as she bit her lower lip and looked me dead in my eyes.

Knowing she planned on getting that morning-after pill, I decided to bust all inside her. Ten minutes later, Joyce was on her second orgasm, and I was pumping full throttle, causing my dick to have a volcanic eruption inside her.

After we finished, we ate, and Joyce was right; I have no idea what the dish was called, but I loved it. I washed the meal down with a glass of orange juice and realized my bladder was full, so I went to relieve myself.

When I returned from the bathroom, Joyce was in the living room watching the news. At first, I paid it no attention, until I heard something about a shooting in Pittsburg. That caught my attention, and I glanced at the TV screen; I seen Kaydah's whip T-boned in the middle of an intersection, and riddled with bullet holes.

"Fuck! I gotta go!" was all I said. I was dressed and out the door in a flash.

CHAPTER 29

One morning, after picking his son up from his baby-momma's spot, Kaydah was on his way back to the hood when some of our opps caught him slippin' at a red light. A nigga in a ski mask bounced out wit' a chop and started chewing his whip up: Tat! Tat! Tat! Tat! Tat!

He hit the gas, running the red light, and ended up getting T-boned by a work truck. He instantly remembered his son was sitting in a car seat, and he looked in the back to check on the lil' man. What he seen shattered his whole world; his baby boy was slumped over, dead from a bullet wound to the head. The K bullet basically took the lil' nigga's whole head off.

Once the Mob got word of what happened, we were on the hunt for whoever was responsible. We had shooters on standby, ready to kill women, children, hustla's, hitters, the good, the bad, and the ugly. It didn't matter, anybody could get it!

Naturally, Kaydah blamed himself, and was grief-stricken like I never thought possible. Sadly, he felt the pain that that too many mothers and fathers had to feel in the hood, the exact pain he himself had caused many mothers and fathers. A pain like no other. But the fact that his lil' man was only a helpless baby seemed to magnify his pain by a million.

The next day, I knew that big bruh needed some support from a loved one; so I was blowing up his phone, to no avail. I called and called, but it would only ring until the answering machine picked up. So I said, "Fuck it!" and decided to slide over to his house and check on him.

When I got there, I didn't even bother to knock. I was the only person he trusted with a key to his spot, and he'd given me one a few years back. So, I let myself in.

As I stepped in, an awful odor invaded my nostrils. I knew the distinct smell very well, and instantly, worry sunk in. I made my way through the house, following the scent to the back bedroom. When I walked in, what I'd feared was before my eyes; my big bruh Kaydah had a crack pipe to his lips and he was blasting off to outer space.

Honestly, I would have preferred to find him dead. Because once you get hooked on crack, you become a whole new person, and the old you is essentially dead anyway!

"What the fuck you doin', nigga," I yelled, disgusted by what I was seeing. Kaydah just dropped the pipe and stared at me blankly. He already had the look of a rock-zombie, one only a crackhead on a serious binge would have.

"I had to shake the pain, my young nigga! I had to!" he finally slurred, in a voice that was barely audible.

I just shook my head in disgust and left him there to face his demons all alone.

CHAPTER 30

On the outside, Kaydah seemed to be back to his old self; grinding and getting money. He swore he wasn't fucking with the base-rock, but his eyes told me a whole different story. That rock is a devil of its own, and once you give it your soul, the odds of breaking its grip are slim-to-none.

I could tell bruh was tryna fight it, but even if he won a battle here and there, I seriously doubted he would win the war against his crack addiction.

I couldn't give up on him, though. There wasn't a war in the world I wouldn't fight with Kaydah, so I did everything I could to keep him from falling victim to the temptation of another hit. But the fact of the matter was, we were in the crack game, and everyone knows you can't sell what you use!

One day Kaydah came to me with some script about how he got robbed for his re-up money. I knew better and had my doubts. But against my better judgment, I decided to give him the benefit of the doubt. Only because there was no way in the world he could've smoked all that damn money.

He wanted to go with me on a lick I'd been plotting on for a while. I did need a getaway driver, so I reluctantly agreed!

Back in the day, when I was 10 years old, my momma was dating some nigga that worked at a liquor store on Railroad, right across from a hood called "West Bully." He used to let me go work with him on the night shift. When it was closing time, he would add up all the money in the cash register and then he'd put it in a floor safe that was in the porn aisle of the store.

The aisle ran along the front window and dead-ended to another window. If you were to look out the dead-end window, you would see the barber shop that was directly next door. In the barber shop parking lot, which was on the side of the building, there was a wall. On the other side of that wall was an alleyway.

So, the plan was to park around the corner until closing time, then I would hop out and creep up to the cuts of the barber shop where the liquor store worker couldn't see me. From that cut-spot, I could peek into the window and see when the worker opened the floor safe. As soon as he opened it and pulled out the potato sack with the money in it, I would shoot out the window. Next, I would climb in through the shattered window and hold the store clerk at gunpoint while I take the sack full of money, and the money he'd counted from the register.

As the getaway driver, Kaydah's job would be to stay parked around the corner until he heard the gun shots. Then, he would pull the car into the alleyway, stopping on the other side of the parking lot wall to wait for me.

Once I jumped back out the window with the money, I would run around the corner through the parking lot, and I'd jump over the wall. After, I'm in the getaway car and we'd be gone! Plain and simple.

$$$$$

At closing time I jumped out the car and pushed to the tuck spot, lowering my ski-mask. He must've closed a little early, because he was already walking back to the floor-safe with the potato sack in hand. *Perfect*, I thought, because now all I had to do was grab the sack and go, since the register money was already in it.

Boom! Boom!

I shot out the window, and had initially expected the clerk to freeze up, while I jumped in and took the money. But once I shot the window out, he ran! I knew there was a .357 revolver tucked by the register, and that's where he was headed, so I had no choice:

Boom! Boom!

I hit the nigga two times in his back, before he could even make it out the aisle. He screamed as he fell, and I made my move: I jumped through the window, grabbed the sack of money, made my exit, dipped through the parking lot, hopped the wall, and before I even had the passenger door shut, Kaydah was peeling out of there, kicking up dust and gravel behind us.

We came up on a quick thirty-eight bands. Nineteen thousand apiece in ten minutes flat!

CHAPTER 31

I was ready to put a play in motion and re-up on something heavy. So, I was headed to my spot to retrieve the money from the jack move, along with some of what I already had stacked. As I was getting close to my block, I muted my slap. This was something I always did, because I don't like bringing extra attention to my spot. I bent the turn on my block and pulled into my driveway. As I was walking up to my front door, I noticed it was cracked open.

I pulled my hammer out, because I always closed and locked my door when I left. It being cracked open only meant one thing; somebody ran up in my shit and could possibly still be inside.

I crept in, both hands grippin' my hammer, while I kept it pointed in front of me. As I looked around my living room, I realized nothing was moved or ransacked. I continued in a stealthy fashion, and listened intently for any noise or movement coming from inside. I heard nothing.

I opened the first bedroom door, nothing moved and there was no one in sight. I opened the second bedroom door, again nothing was moved and there was no one in sight. Then I peeked into the bathroom, which was open already, nothing. Finally, I opened the door to my master bedroom, and stopped dead in my tracks: "What the fuck?" I said out loud, as I seen my closet door, which needed a key, was wide open! *I know this nigga isn't that far gone!* I thought, as I made my way into my walk-in closet. Sure enough, the secret door to my hidden room was wide open. I looked in and my big-ass, bolted-down safe was left open and empty!

All I could do was shake my head in disgust as anger came over me. It could've only been one nigga: Kaydah! He was the only one I trusted, and he had the keys to my spot and closet door. He also was the only one who knew about the secret room and knew the combo to my safe; just as I was the only one he trusted with the combo to his!

The reason we swapped combos was just in case one of use got locked up or killed. You have to be realistic and understand that those risks come with the game. In the event one of those unfortunate circumstances took place, we knew the money would go to lawyer fees or funeral and burial costs, and anything left over would go to family. The guns and dope would go to whoever was still out or alive. We had all bases covered and fully trusted one another. But this wasn't Kaydah I was dealing with; it was a crackhead in Kaydah's body!

It was obvious it was him, but what upset me the most was that he didn't even try to hide the fact that it was him by making it look like a burglary or something. It was as if he was saying: "Yeah, nigga,

I jacked you! What you gonna do about it?" Them hungry-ass monkeys on bruh's back, definitely got the best of him. His new-found love of rock allowed him to abandon all his morals.

At that moment, my big bruh Kaydah was no longer my family; he withered away mentally and became my opposition. That realization set in and Kaydah's own words popped in my head. "Never, and I do mean never, let anybody play you like a sucka' 'bout yo' money. The first dumb mutha'fucka' to try you, is the one you make an example out of." He told me that years ago, and it looks like those words were gonna come back to haunt him.

"I gotta kill this nigga," I spoke whole-heartedly to myself.

CHAPTER 32

Kaydah had taught me everything I knew about the game. Since I was knee-high to a grasshopper he'd been grooming me for this exact moment. He understood that the game consisted of winning or losing – kill or be killed. But nobody in their right mind would've expected a twist like this one; especially not Kaydah, or myself! He preached trust and loyalty to me like it was God. Everything we'd built together in them streets was built on trust and loyalty. But that was over now. Big bruh had played the game like an all-star for many years, and now the game had played him. His judgment day had arrived.

$$$$

I knew Kaydah would be in the projects, posted up in the back parking lot with others from the Mob, as was customary. So, I grabbed a throw-away .40 Glock I had tucked, and made my way to the parking lot. As I got close I was mumbling to myself about how Kaydah had forced my hand by robbing me, and now he had to pay for that.

In my young mind, murder wasn't fully understood yet; all I knew was that my mind was set and nothing was going to stop me from doing what I had to do. As I walked up, I seen the Mob posted up about twenty deep.

Kaydah was standing there smoking a blunt, surrounded by loved ones, without a care in the world. That's how it was supposed to be, nobody could slide up trippin' without catching a few hundred rounds; except I wasn't a nobody, I'm family and that's why you don't cross family!

I put my hand into my hoodie pocket and felt the cold-heaviness of the cannon. For the first time I felt my trigger finger begin to itch. I forced everything out of my mind as I pushed up on the crowd. It was as if I was in a haze. When I pulled the banger out, I snapped out of it, and a wave of fire came over me. At that point, I was high on adrenaline, and didn't care who was watching. In fact, I wanted to make a statement in front of them all. I intended on showing the whole Mob that I'm not to be fucked with.

The Mob started trying to greet me, but I was zeroed in on my target. Niggas noticed the look in my eyes before they noticed the gun in my hand. Then, Kaydah spotted me and to my surprise – he smiled. This infuriated me even more. *What this nigga think I'm playin'?* I thought to myself, as I walked right up on him and shot him once in the chest. Boom!

The force of the .40 cal ripping through his chest and out his back caused him to fold up like a lawn-chair. A small whimper escaped his mouth as he held his chest in pain.

"You really thought you was gonna jack me and get away wit' it, like I'm some sucka? … You got me fucked up! … Out of all people, you should know you raised me better than that!" I growled with pure anger in my voice.

To my amazement, with a bullet hole in his chest and all, Kaydah flashed me another smile. *This nigga really done lost it*, I thought, before I put a bullet in my big bruh's top, rocking him to sleep forever.

CHAPTER 33

The Mob were stunned, watching in awe as I took out my big bruh Kaydah; a legend in the streets. Even though I was only 20 years old, they knew they'd just witnessed a young boss at work. My own legend was growing amongst my peers, and I didn't even realize it. I followed the rules of the game with precision and loyalty, exactly how you're supposed to. That's how respect is earned in the Mob.

"We the Mob! We family, and family don't break the rules that our foundation is built on! That nigga stole from me, and he had to pay for that. Period!" With that statement and the Mob's undivided attention, I walked up on Kaydah's lifeless body and slowly removed the famous Mob chain from around his neck: "I'm sorry, big bruh, but you fucked up," I whispered, as a single tear dropped; I clenched my teeth so tightly that the muscles in my jaw began to bulge. Then, I put the chain around my neck as if it had been mine all along.

"Kaydah always told me this would be my chain one day," I stated, as the Mob stared at me in awe.

They knew the legend of the two niggas who'd previously represented the Mob chain, and what they meant to our existence. I followed their eyes down to it; as it dangled just below my chest, flashes of Kaydah and all the years we mobbed together since I was just a kid hit me at once!

Once I broke the trance, I immediately felt a sense of honor to be the one representing it now! Officially my position was elevated from a Mob "member" to a Mob "Boss." I just hated that it was the result of me having to kill my big bruh, but the game was grimy like that!

After I exited through the speechless crowd of thugs, I didn't know what to do. Then, my instincts kicked in: I went straight to Kaydah's to try and recover what was left of my money.

By the time I'd gotten to his door, the sun was already beginning to set. It was a blistering hot day, so now that it was cooling off, the streets were starting to come alive with people. I knew I had to get in and get out before too many people noticed me leaving with duffel bags and whatnot. But then again, it was probably too late for that.

"What's up, Paperboy?" one of the neighbors asked, oblivious to what had transpired only moments ago.

"Nothin' much, same shit, different day, you know how it goes."

"That I do …"

I stepped in and a strange feeling took over my body. For some reason I felt as if Kaydah was right there in the spot with me. I don't know much about ghosts and spirits and all that shit, so maybe he was?

I quickly shook off the feeling and made my way to his safe. We both had the same setup, with a secret room hidden behind a trap door in the closet.

As I was looking around, I realized all of bruh's valuables were still in place – the big projector style TV, the stereo system, and everything else. I hadn't been to the bruh's crib since I'd caught him smoking rock. So with him robbing me and everything, I guess I figured he'd clucked all his shit already, but nope, everything was exactly how I remembered it.

When I walked into the closet, the door to the secret room was left open, just as mine was. I didn't pay that much attention, though, and went straight to the safe. As I was working the combination, I spoke out loud: "Please let this nigga still have my money. There's no way he could've blown it overnight."

CLANK ! The safe unlocked and I pulled it open.

CHAPTER 34

My heart stopped and my jaw hit the floor. I couldn't believe my eyes; the safe wasn't empty! In fact, that big mutha' fucka' was full to the top! There was so much money crammed in that safe, I was dumbfounded. This shit didn't make any sense! As I was trying to comprehend what I was seeing, something caught my eye; it was a folded piece of paper with my name on it.

I grabbed the paper, opened it, and started reading:

My young nigga! obviously you know I'm dead, because you handled your business like a real nigga's supposed to. I could never steal from you, my young nigga, you've always been like a son to me. I only made it appear that way, because I couldn't allow myself to continue living on this earth as a dope fiend. It was only a matter of time before the addiction consumed me, and I could never allow myself to be remembered as such! But truth be told, from the very first hit I was hooked. It didn't matter how hard I tried, I couldn't get that monkey off my back. So I "robbed" you, and made sure you knew it was me. I knew you would buy it, because you and only you knew of my secret addiction, and what that shit does to a person and their morals. I also know how I raised you, and everything I taught you about trust and loyalty. That crossing that line was the ultimate of betrayal; punishable by death! I knew you wouldn't let that slide, because you know I wouldn't let that slide.

I know you're probably wondering why I didn't put myself out of my own misery? I also couldn't allow myself to be seen as taking the coward's way out. So after I finish this letter, I'ma go to the parking lot and spend my last minutes with the Mob while I wait for what I got coming. I can see the demo now, and the shock left on the faces of the Mob ..."

After reading that part, I stopped and envisioned him smiling before and after I shot him. At the time, I took it as disrespect, but now it made perfect sense: he was smiling because in his tormented mind, he knew he'd raised me right – it was the smile of a proud father!

" ... I love you, Paperboy, don't ever forget it! Everything in the safe is yours. I left you well over a million dollars, not counting your money. I trust you'll remember the many lessons I taught you as you represent that Mob chain around your neck to the fullest! A new legend is born! My last wish is to be cremated (I never liked the thought of being six feet

under) and to have my ashes mixed with my son's, and spread 'em in the bay for me ..."

I looked down and seen the urn with his son's ashes ...

"Always remember: we live for the Mob, we die for the Mob! 1 Love, 1 Mob
  Kaydah"

By the time I was done reading the letter, I realized I had tears streaming down my face. Kaydah really fucked me up with this twist. I would never be able to fathom why he had me take him out the way he did. But it was what he wanted, so I refused to blame myself! Deep down, though, I'll always be mad at him for it! As selfish as he was in the way he went about it, he sure did make sure he left me in a position of money and power!

CHAPTER 35

After I read the letter, reality kicked back in and I realized I had a shit load of money I needed to move – fast! I literally had no way of moving it all at once, and I couldn't trust anybody to help me, so I had to think fast.

I wanted to move it all in one trip. So I knew I needed a truck or a van. I instantly thought of Auntie "Umm Hmm", as we called her on the block, because her crackhead ass was always saying "Umm Hmm". It didn't matter what you were doing, she would be driving by, stop, look at you like you were doing something wrong, and then she'd give you her signature "Umm Hmm", before she drove off. Other than that, the only words that came out of her mouth were "I need a nickel," or "I need a dime."

Anyway, she had a hooptie-ass van that I knew she would let me use without question for a fat-ass rock. So, I went straight to Auntie "Umm Hmm" down the block with a fat rock and came back with the van. I pulled it right up onto the lawn as close to the door as possible, and slid the side door open.

Then, I went in and started loading up trash bags, duffel bags, and pillow cases with the money. Once all the money was bagged up, I started loading it into the van. After the van was loaded with the money, I grabbed all the guns and Kaydah's son's ashes. Then I heard his pit bark. ...

I hopped in the van and smashed to my tuck house in Parkside. I pulled up, opened the garage, pulled in and just sat there for a while lost in the haze of my thoughts. I couldn't believe what had all transpired, my whole world would be different from this day forward. As I played the events over and over in my mind, I knew they'd changed me and my life forever. Kaydah had undeniably taught me something that would forever be engraved inside me; Kaydah taught me how to kill.

I needed a blunt! So I got out the van, closed the garage, and went inside to blaze something fat. After I smoked, I unloaded the money and guns, then I took a quick trip over the Antioch Bridge to toss the murder weapon. Afterwards, I took Auntie "Umm Hmm" her van back, slid her a few more rocks, and went straight to my momma's house to pass out. I was drained and exhausted in every way possible: physically, mentally, and emotionally!

CHAPTER 36

The cops were banging on the door, at ten the next morning. My momma was already up watching the breaking news as the reporters talked about the homicide that had occurred in the back of our projects.

"Who the fuck is banging on my door like the mu' fuckin' police?" she asked, as she snatched the door open with attitude. To her surprise, it WAS the police. Two middle-aged white men in suits with badges hanging from their necks. Both of them had potbellies and buzz cuts.

"Hello, ma'am. We're with the Pittsburg Police Department's homicide unit. I'm detective Letherman, and this is my partner, Detective Jones. We need to speak with your son about a homicide that occurred last night," the shorter officer said.

"Homicide? My boy doesn't know anything about no homicide," my momma snapped at the officer.

"Listen, we just want to ask him a couple quick questions, that's all," the taller officer added.

"Fuck that! Y'all don't need to talk to my boy about shit," she barked confidently as she began to close the door. Just before the door shut, one of the detectives put his foot inside, stopping it.

"Look, we can do this the easy way or the hard way. We only need twenty minutes to get a warrant to come in and get him. He's not in any trouble, we just want to ask him some questions."

My momma thought about putting up a fight, but then she thought about the crack pipes and other drug paraphernalia she had scattered around the house. She didn't want Child Protective Services trying to take my younger siblings away. So, she reluctantly let them in: "Make it quick" she spat, as she stepped to the side. "I'ma wake him up."

"Don't worry, Ma'am, we will," the taller officer assured her. The two walked in and went to sit on the couch.

"Don't even bother sitting down. Y'all won't be here long enough to get comfortable," she stressed, stopping the detectives in mid-squat. "I'll go get him," she continued. My momma snatched my ass outta bed by the neck of my shirt.

"What the fuck?" I mumbled, still half asleep, while she dragged me into the living room. As I stepped into the living room, I was surprised to see the two pigs standing there. That caught my attention and woke my game up.

"These detectives said they need to ask you some questions," my momma informed me.

"About what?" I wondered out loud.

"I'm Detective Letherman, and this is my partner. We need to ask you about Kaydah," one of them said as he pulled out a notebook.

I just stayed quiet and stared at them like I was confused.

"When was the last time you saw Kaydah?" the other detective asked.

I shrugged my shoulders before I spoke. "I don't know, a couple days ago maybe." I answered without emotion.

We were told you were seen coming out of his place last night?" the detective quizzed.

"Naw, wasn't me. Why, what's going on?" I asked, trying to appear confused.

"Are you positive?" the other detective asked.

"Yeah, I am. Now, can you tell me what' going on," I demanded.

"Well, he was found murdered last night with multiple gunshot wounds. You know anything about that?" he persisted.

"That's crazy! Naw, man, I don't know a thing about that!" I responded, sounding shocked.

"Well, that takes care of that," my momma said, putting an end to their questioning. She went to the door and opened it. Then, she stepped to the side, giving them a clear path out.

The detective had no choice but to leave, and were obviously heated: "We'll be in contact," Letherman concluded as they walked past my momma.

"Have a nice day," she said, as she slammed the door almost hitting the shorter one where the good Lord split him. "What the fuck was that about?" my momma asked, looking me directly in the eyes. She was trembling, but had hidden it well from the pigs.

"I have no idea," I lied. Then I faded back into my room and took a deep breath. When it came to my momma, I usually held back nothing. I answered her questions truthfully, wanting to give it to her straight before she could hear it from the streets. She knew her son was a drug dealer and a product of the streets. But in her eyes, I couldn't do no wrong. She loved how I always put our family first and treated her with respect at all times. But under these circumstances, there was no way I was going to tell her the truth. Shit, it was bad enough I let my anger get the best of me and did what I did in front of a crowd. All I could do was hope it didn't come back to haunt me.

CHAPTER 37

Now that Kaydah was gone, there was a major void in the drug game, and I'd planned on filling it. Kaydah left me with all that money, and I was going to do big things with it. The only problem was, I didn't have a connect. Kaydah's connect died with him, so I had to find one of my own A.S.A.P.!

I hollered at Kendra, and she had a small-time connect in 'Frisco that went by "Hardball". The nigga wouldn't sell anything over a quarter-pound at a time. He also charged top dollar for work that was stepped-on, but it would have to work for now! So, I was snatching up the four zips, and whipping it up in the kitchen myself, just to keep things flowing until I found an official connect. Which was easier said than done, because young niggas in the "P" had a bad rep and were known as Stick-Up-Kids that robbed connects.

Leave it to simple-minded hot-heads to fuck shit off for the real go-getta's, I thought to myself, frustrated. But I would find a connect; believe that! In the meantime, though, I was on my way to spread

Kaydah's and his son's ashes in the bay, their final resting place together, just as Kaydah had wished.

$$$$$

There was this older Mexican cat that I was constantly crossing paths with. It seemed like everywhere I went, I'd see him and he'd see me. He'd always be driving something different; one day it'd be a K-5, a Ford F-150 the next, then a Chevy Silverado. But he was always driving some type of truck, and he was always dressed as a cowboy. He'd have his cowboy hat, big belt buckle, and snake-skin boots, complemented by gold chains and rings.

I'd see him and nod my head, and he'd return the gesture. There seemed to be a natural respect between us, even though we didn't know one another. In the back of my mind, I just knew he was in the drug trade, most likely cartel of some sort.

One night, I was pulling into the Broken Wheel Bar in Oakley, California, to run a play, when I spotted the older Mexican walking out. I threw up the "deuces", as if to say "What's up," and he responded by lifting his hand and nodding. This was my chance, assuming he was a connect; I had to make my move and see if he'd fuck with me.

I waved my hand in a motion signaling for him to "Come here." He paused for a second, and then made his way over. I knew from experience that most Mexicans are not particularly fond of my kind, but I also knew they recognized a thoroughbred hustla' at first sight. Under such circumstances, they don't see black, they see money!

"What's up, amigo?" he asked, speaking good English.

"Look, boss, I'ma be direct and straight forward with you. I'ma businessman with a lot of money to spend, and I'm looking for a new connect on coke," I admitted bluntly. He was quiet for a second obviously thinking; I added: "I'm not with the games, and I do official business. It's just my last connect got killed, so I'm in a tough spot," I said, interrupting his thought process and looking him directly in his eyes. He continued thinking.

"You busy, amigo?" he finally asked.

"Not at all." I lied, not wanting to lose a potential connect over some chump change.

"Leave your carro and come with me, yeah?" he asked, pointing towards a green F-150.

"OK, no problem," I agreed.

"No pistola, amigo," he demanded.

I pulled my thang off my lap from under my shirt and tucked it under my seat right in front of him. Then I got out and we headed towards his truck.

CHAPTER 38

We hit the back streets and he took me to some house in the cuts of Oakley: "Come inside, amigo, and we talk," he said.

We got out and I followed him inside. The house was mostly empty except for a long oval kitchen table in the middle of the living room with some chairs around it. No TV, no couches. Nothing.

"Grab a seat, amigo." He pulled out a chair at the far end of the table, and then he walked into the kitchen. I sat down and waited, hoping that the conversation would end with me having a new plug.

He came back carrying a bottle of tequila and two glass cups with ice in them. He put one of the cups in front of me and filled it up, not even asking if I wanted some. As he poured, I noticed what looked like a worm swimming around inside the bottle.

"What the fuck!? Is that a worm?" I asked in a curious but shocked tone.

"Sí, amigo. It won't hurt you," he laughed. Then, he sat down and filled up his glass as well. He noticed I hadn't drunk any of mine, and lifted up his glass, taking a big swig. I followed suit. The liquor fired up my chest, but I kept a straight face, not wanting to look like lightweight.

"What's your name, amigo?" he asked.

"Paperboy," I responded.

"Paperboy? How do you get a name like Paperboy?" he asked, obviously trying to make small talk.

I shrugged my shoulder as if I didn't know, because it wasn't important: "What's your name?" I asked, instead.

"Pelón." He lifted up his hat as he responded. "As you can see," he chuckled, revealing a smooth bald head.

"So, Pelón means bald?" I asked, making the connection.

"So how old are you, amigo?" he asked.

"I'm 20." I answered truthfully figuring there was no reason to lie about my age.

"20, Aye? When I was 20 I was chasing chicas, not money. But I soon realized if you had the money, the chicas chased you," he joked, keeping it real.

"Ain't that the truth," I agreed with a smile.

Pelón took another swig of his tequila, finishing it off. I did the same. This caused Pelón to stand up and refill both glasses before he sat back down: "Amigo, I've seen you around, and you are different than most of your kind. You pay attention and you see me as well. Most pay me no attention, but not you; you show respect and acknowledge me. I like that!" he paused, taking a drink of his tequila before continuing: "I can tell you are a business man about your dinero, but I want to make sure you know I no small time. If you want to do business with me, amigo, it's big business. Comprende?" he asked, looking me dead in my eyes the whole time.

It was obvious I was in the presence of money and power, and even in my young mind, I knew the potential of such a situation. Kaydah's words came to me from the past, as if his ghost was whispering them in my ear. "Always be a boss in the presence of a boss. That way, even if he outweighs you in the game, you keep him off balance. Because when he recognizes another boss is in front of him, you gain leverage," I remembered Kaydah explaining years ago.

"Yes, Pelón, I do understand," I said, matching his stare and taking a drink of my tequila before continuing: "I know I am young, but I am not small time myself. I need a connect on big weight, amigo," I stated with confidence.

CHAPTER 39

"OK, amigo, then we can do business. It's going to be $17,500 a kilo. Cocaine so pure you can turn one into two and it'll still be the best product in the streets," Pelón bragged, making me an offer.

Things were going better than I could've even imagined. I knew this was my opportunity to showcase my boss status: "Give 'em to me for $15,000 apiece, and I'll by ten kilos," I countered, letting him know I wasn't small time.

Pelón paused, seemingly impressed by my counter offer. He probably thought I would only want one or two. After a few seconds, he spoke: "I'll tell you what, amigo – I'll give them to you for $15,000 a kilo, but you have to buy twenty! Otherwise, it'll be $16,500 for ten," he responded with a counter of his own, obviously trying to see if I was indeed playing in the big leagues.

"Twenty it is, we have a deal!" I accepted his offer with no hesitation, letting him know I was serious. Then, I stood up and extended my hand to seal the deal.

He stood and shook my hand, matching my grip: "I'm very impressed, amigo," he said, releasing my hand and picking up his glass: "Saludo," he said, extending it to me.

I picked my glass up and extended it to his, so that our glasses connected with a "clink": "Saludo," I responded, hoping I said it right.

"Okay, amigo, meet me here tomorrow morning at five a.m. and we'll do the deal. I'll be introducing you to my Primo. From then on, you'll work directly with him," he said, informing me of the time and place for our transaction.

"I'll be here," I agreed.

"Come alone, amigo, and no funny business; my Primo and his amigos will be heavily armed," he instructed sternly.

"Understood. We'll be doing good business," I assured him.

"Vamanos, I'll take you to your carro," he said, concluding our first meeting. And like that, I was connected with a plug on kilos of pure cocaine.

CHAPTER 40

I had so much dope, there was no way I could sell it all servin' knocks. It was time to put my team on! Besides, one thing I know to be factual; you always gotta let your team eat. You gotta let them be bosses in their own right. If you don't, they'll resent you and envy your position. So I was going to make sure my team felt equal. Because the fact is, we're the Mob and the Mob is a unit! That's how love stays strong and loyalty is built.

I wanted all my niggas to eat with me, of course; but at the same time, the D-Game isn't for everybody. I needed assets, not liabilities, which wouldn't be too hard to find. Not only had Kaydah put in work and sold dope for many years, he also worked hard to surround the Mob with real niggas that respected the Mob and the game as much as he did. So, even though he was gone, a big part of his heart and soul was still present and now under my leadership. As long as the Mob existed, Kaydah was still alive, living through us.

My thoughts drifted off to Kaydah and some of his words of wisdom: "treat a man as he is, and he will remain as he is; treat a man as he can and should be, and he will become that." So, as the new leader of the Mob, I had to look at my brothers with the eye of what they're capable of, and treat them in terms of their potential. That's exactly what I was going to do.

I had twenty kilos of pure cocaine to work with, so I decided to pick ten hustla's that I felt had the most potential, and I'd front each a kilo. They would have to bring me thirty bands back and stack the rest of the profit. Once they paid me the thirty bands, I'd front them each another kick for the same amount. After that, they should easily have enough to pay me my thirty bands and buy one for thirty. That's exactly how I broke it down to them: "I'm only going to front you twice. After you pay me for the second brick, if you don't have enough to buy one yourself, you're cut off! Each brick is 100% pure, so make sure you step on it and turn it into two bricks. It'll still be the best product around, guaranteed! So, technically speaking, you're getting two bricks for the thirty bands."

After the second brick, everyone was ready to buy their own, except two individuals: Kendra and my nigga Jacka. They were ready to purchase their own brick after the *first* one I'd fronted them. They brought me sixty bands apiece, separating their selves from the pack. So I sold them the one and gave them my word that I'd bring them two more on 'front' as soon as I re-upped. Which I did that same day, so they ended up with three kicks apiece. Which of course, was actually six kicks apiece.

My nigga Jacka was a young hardheaded go-getta' that was coming out of the trenches of the Lo. He had a lot of potential and I was going to bring it out of him. His days of running wild in the streets were done. Now, it was time to take them streets over.

$$$$$

Within three months, my stature in the D-Game was elevated above all else in my region. The Mob had the best work and the best prices, so we were knocking off our competition with ease. I knew this would cause a lot of hate and put a target on my back, but I wasn't tripping. It comes with the ethics of the game: for every nigga ballin', there's a hunnid broke niggas. So I knew that I was an obvious target for all the Stick-Up-Kids hungry for their next lick. But I know the game, and respect it enough to stay prepared at all times. *Let 'em try,* I would think to myself, as I gripped the hammer on my lap. Like the saying goes: "If you stay ready, you don't gotta get ready." And I was always ready for whatever!

CHAPTER 41

One day I got a call from the 'Frisco nigga "Hardball" that Kendra had us getting our product from before I'd met Pelón.

"What's good, bruh?" I asked.

"Paper, I got a business proposition for you," he stated.

"Oh, yeah? Well, I'm all ears. Or do we have to meet up?" I asked, because we don't talk about anything hot over the phone.

"We definitely gotta meet up for this, my nigga," he said, informing me that the matter was indeed hot.

"It's all good, just let me know when you hit the P and I'll pull up on you," I responded, letting him know he was going to have to come to me.

"I'm on my way. I'll be hitting yo' line soon."

"Fo' sho', hit me."

About 45 minutes later, he hit me back; I gave him the where: "Hit the Railroad exit, bust a left, and go straight until you see the park on the left. Pull into the parking lot, and you'll see me sitting in my seven-deuce Chev with the top down," I directed when I answered.

"Got it."

After killing Kaydah, I really didn't wanna drive the Coug-nut any more, because it reminded me of him too much. So, I parked it in my garage at the Parkside house and cashed out for an all-original '72 convertible Chev.

About five minutes later I seen a money-green 5.0 convertible pulling in.

"That mu'fucka' clean," I admitted out loud to myself. It was Hardball, and he pulled right up next to me. I was about halfway done with the blunt I was smoking: "Hop in," I hollered at him. He jumped in the passenger seat, and I passed him the blunt: "Hit this. It's that white widow." He did, and he passed it back.

"Bruh, I need a new connect. Mine got caught up by the Feds, and I'm losing money," he spat out, skipping the bullshit.

"That don't sound like a business proposition," I pointed out.

"Hear me out; if you can plug me wit' a connect on the kicks, I'll cash you out ten bands for the introduction," he proposed. I could tell he was desperate.

"That's not enough," I responded.

"Fuck it, I'll give you fifteen bands. Work wit' me, bruh," he pleaded.

He did all his hustling in 'Frisco, so he wouldn't be taking no money out of my pockets: "I'll holla' at my connect and see if he's interested. If he is, I'll make the introduction. But I'ma need the fifteen bands and the 'stang," I said, referring to the 5.0 he was driving.

"Bet," he said, with no hesitation.

"You got the money on you right now?" I asked.

"All hunnids," he responded.

"Go to the mall or something, and I'ma see what I can do. I'll hit you as soon as I get a thumbs up or a thumbs down."

$$$$$

I don't know, amigo, I don't like doing business with just anybody," Pelón said, unsure.

"I understand that, it's completely up to you. I've done good business with him in the past, and I know he has good money," I responded, trying to sway his decision.

"You know what, amigo, if you say he's good business, then we can do business," he agreed hesitantly.

"Okay, I'll let him know it's all good," I said.

"Take him to meet Primo; I will let Primo know it's bueno. But if Primo gets a bad vibe from him, no más!" he stated firmly.

"That's not a problem, amigo, I understand," I replied.

CHAPTER 42

I called Hardball and told him to meet me back at the park. Which meant it was all good, otherwise I would've told him to take his ass back to 'Frisco.

"I'm on my way right now," he said, and I could hear the excitement in his voice.

On my way back to the park, I stopped by the hood real quick; the Lo was right around the corner from the park anyway. I slid up on my lil' nigga Husalah, who'd been talking 'bout getting my Chev from me since I got it.

"What's good, Hus', you still want the Chev?" I asked him.

"Hell, yeah! You ready to sell it to me?" he asked.

"Even better! I'ma trade it to you for yo' bucket," I laughed, referring to his Toyota.

"Nigga, quit playin'," he said, thinking I was joking.

"Naw, real talk," I parked it, got out, and tossed him the keys: "Now, where's the keys to my bucket?" I asked.

130

"No trade-backs, nigga," Hus' declared as he tossed me the keys to his bucket-ass Toyota Corolla.

I jumped in the Toyota and gassed off to meet Hardball. When he pulled into the parking lot, I was standing on the sidewalk smoking another blunt. He parked and got out.

"So, everything's good?" he asked anxiously.

"Yeah, bruh, I got you plugged in. I gotta take you to meet Primo," I answered, passing him the blunt.

"Fa' sho'! Good lookin' out, my nigga," he beamed with a smile, as he took the blunt.

"It's all good! But first, I need my money and the keys to my car," I demanded.

"How'd I know you was going to say that?" he shook his head: "The money is in the glovebox, and the keys are in the ignition. But how am I gonna get back to the city?" he continued.

"I don't know, bruh. That ain't my problem," I joked. "Naw! I'm just fuckin' wit' you. Consider it a trade," I said, handing him the keys to the bucket.

"What these go to?" he asked, confused.

"Yo' new ride," I said, pointing to the bucket, which I parked at the end of the parking lot.

"Oh, hell naw!" he laughed, "Will that bitch even make it to the city?" he asked, seriously.

"Only one way to find out," I started laughing myself. "Don't trip, though, you're riding wit' me to go meet your new plug," I said, as I went to jump in my new 'Stang.

Before I even started it, I grabbed the money out of the glove box. Hardball sat quietly, hitting the blunt, while I counted. Just as he said, it was one hundred and fifty crispy Benjamin Franklins: fifteen bands! Once I was done counting, I put the money back in the glove box, and he passed me my blunt, which was more like a doobie now, so I hit it one last time and tossed it: "Let's roll," I said, as the engine sparked into a roar.

I introduced Hardball to Primo; they talked business and swapped numbers. Everything was straight, so I took bruh back to his bucket and he was on his way back to 'Frisco. Well, he was going to attempt to make it back to 'Frisco, anyway.

I slid out the park and pulled back up on my lil' nigga Husalah in my new 5.0.

"Damn, Paper, that mu'fucka' dope! How much you pay fo' it?" he asked, admiring my shit.

"You wouldn't believe me if I told you," I replied.

"Well, tell me anyway. How much?" he asked even more curious now.

I didn't pay anything. I traded yo' bucket for it," I smiled.

"Nigga, you always playin'." Hus' laughed while shaking his head.

"Told you you wouldn't believe me," I said. Then I gassed off, leaving him in a cloud of smoke, as I burned rubber all the way down the block.

CHAPTER 43

My nigga "Teardrop" hit my line talking about: "I'm ready for you, bruh," which meant he was ready for me to drop more work on him. He was one of the "ten" Mob members that I'd fronted the kicks to, and he was in the process of taking over the dope game in the "Brownies" and the areas surrounding it. The "Brownies" was what we called an apartment complex by the Walmart in the P, because of the dark brown paint.

He had an apartment rented in his bitch's name, and he set up shop with a few of his young hitters. They started trappin' out the complex, while the other D-Boys tried to compete. But, word spread like a wildfire amongst the baseheads, that the Mob had not only better quality, but fatter rocks, also! So, in no time, all the baseheads were bringing their money to the Mob, and Teardrop had the Brownies on lock!

At first, Teardrop was grabbing a kick at a time, every month or so. But then things started picking up, and his turnover rate was getting faster and faster. Here he was, ready again, after only a week! *Damn!*

133

He really gots shit locked down, I thought. So, I decided to sell him the one and front him another two on top of it, like I do with Kendra and Jacka.

I pulled up in my new 5.0, top down, and beat knockin'. There was a lil' crowd of niggas posted in the cuts and they were staring with ice-cold glares. One of them I'd recognized; he'd been posted in that exact spot on my last two drops. I figured they were the D-Boys the Mob was competing with, even though it was obvious there was no competition.

My street senses kicked in and I reached to my lap, where my banger rested. Matching their glare, I bounced out with the gun in my hand. Then, I tucked it on my waistline, letting them niggas know I wasn't slippin'. It was a suffocating ninety degrees, and I was shirtless, rocking only the Mob chain and my tattoos. I grabbed the backpack with the three bricks of work in it out the back seat and made my way to Teardrop's trap.

"Here goes that work, Mob. You've been movin' shit quick, so I fronted you an extra two bricks on top of it," I informed him of the increase in product as I tossed him the backpack.

"Fa' sho', Mob! Here go the thirty for the one, and I'm have the other sixty for you in a hurry," Teardrop said, handing me thirty bands in a different backpack.

"How 'bout you bring me the whole hunnid and fifty bands when you ready fo' yo' next three bricks?" I suggested.

"That'll work, too! It's all good, Mob," he agreed.

"Just so you know, there's a lil' squad of niggas posted up out there. They was muggin' as I slid up," I said, giving him a head's up.

"Yeah, them niggas out there tryna' short-stop with them lil'-ass rocks they got. They salty, 'cause all their knocks started coming to us for the boulders. They don't want no funk, though," he stated with his usual cockiness.

"Fa' sho', Mob. Just stay on toes," I cautioned, before I walked out. As I went to my whip, them niggas were nowhere in sight.

CHAPTER 44

A month later, I was back to drop Teardrop another three bricks and pick up the hunnid and fifty bands he had for me. As I pulled in, I spotted the one nigga posted up solo again. This time, instead of muggin', he gave me a lil' nod. I nodded back.

Again, as I was leaving, there was no one in sight. I tossed the backpack of money in the back seat, and as I was getting in the driver seat, I peeped a thick-thang getting out of her car. She caught me looking and flashed a smile as she waved. I backed out the parking spot, and pulled up on her as she was grabbing some shopping bags out of her trunk.

She was bent over, giving me a nice view as she purposely reached deep into the trunk. Her skin-tight booty-shorts left nothing to the imagination and between two exposed ass cheeks, I seen her camel-toe eating up fabric. *Damn!* I thought, as I pulled up so close I could have slapped her ass. She grabbed the last of her bags, closed her trunk, and turned towards me: "Hey, sexy! What's your name?" I asked, as I continued my scan. She was sexy in a ghetto-fabulous kind of way. She had a pretty face with big D.S.L.s (dick sucking lips), covered in lip gloss, and her sleeveless tube-top hugged her big breasts, causing a clear impression of her nipples.

"Wouldn't you like to know?" she asked seductively, as she stepped closer. She was trying to keep a poker face, but I caught her eyes as they quickly shifted towards the back of my whip, like someone was coming. I could almost smell the nigga creeping up on me.

I instinctively pulled my banger from under my shirt. My top was down and I swung around, catching the Stick-Up-Kid off guard. Before he could fully lift his hammer, I let off two shots – Boom! Boom! I heard the bitch scream as I hit the nigga with a buzzer-beater, dropping him instantly.

Right then, a spray of bullets lit my whip up from an upstairs apartment window, and bystanders started to scramble to avoid stray bullets. As the deafening sound of bullets hitting metal vibrated through the vehicle, I ducked low and reached for my door handle. As I went to roll out my seat, I felt a bullet rip through my back and out my chest. I hit the pavement and looked underneath the whip; I seen the legs of another shooter running up – Boom! Boom! I sent a couple hollow-tips into his legs.

"Aghh!" he screamed, as he hit the floor.

Once I seen the gunman go down, I sprung into action and got back to my feet. Even though I knew I was hit, survival instincts and adrenaline took over. I rounded the front of my whip, so I'd have something to duck behind, if needed, and seen that the nigga fumbled his gun when he got tagged. He was trying to reach for it, but I wasn't allowing that – Boom! Boom! I felt like a monster as I smirked while putting two rounds into his face.

I jumped back in my whip, and just as I was gassing off, another spray of bullets came from the apartment window. Tat! Tat! Tat! Tat! Glass flew everywhere as a trail of bullets barely missed my head and thundered through my windshield. I bent a right out of the apartments and heard the 'flapping' of the two flat tires on my passenger side. I started feeling faint from blood loss, and was trying hard not to lose consciousness, while also trying to maintain control of the whip. But it was to no avail, I fought it as long as I could and blacked out!

CHAPTER 45

I woke up the next day, handcuffed to a hospital bed. My eyes gained focus and there was a detective sitting in a chair. At that moment, memories of the shootout flashed in my mind. The detective looked up from the newspaper he was reading and noticed I was awake. Then, he called the doctor.

"How do you feel?" the doctor asked.

"Like a survivor," I answered honestly.

"That you are! You're lucky to be alive, you were shot three times, and one bullet pierced your lung," the doctor revealed to my amazement.

"Three times? I only felt one!" I said in disbelief.

"Yeah, that's a common occurrence in gun battles," the detective chimed in.

"What do you know about gun battles?" I laughed, causing a rush of pain.

"Here, let me help you," the doctor said, pushing the morphine drip button. I felt an instant rush of calmness come over me.

"I have a few questions for you," stated the detective.

"You don't look like my attorney," I pointed out.

"That's because I'm not," he admitted dryly.

"Didn't think so! I don't have anything to say to you."

"That's OK, we have plenty of witnesses." He walked over to me and started reading me my rights: "You have the right to remain silent, …"

"No shit! I'm fuckin' cuffed to a hospital bed," I thought to myself.

"… Do you understand your rights?" he finished.

"Yeah, and I want my attorney," I informed him.

$$$$$

Those witnesses, and the fact that me and my car were both shot up, ended up working in my favor. The eyewitnesses all explained that I was ambushed, and only shot back in self-defense. Whether they realized that I shot first or not, I don't know. But every single one said I shot back in self-defense. So the two bodies were ruled self-defense, and I was sentenced to a County-year for unlawful possession of a firearm and a probation violation. This was my second gun charge, which ain't shit. Mysteriously, the hunnid and fifty bands disappeared; crooked-ass P.P.D. came up on that! So it was back to the County-Jail for me, but this time my name was ringing bells like a church on Sunday.

$$$$$

After I was a few months into my County-bullet, niggas started coming through with different stories

140

from the streets about who was getting money and how. The bosses in the dope game seemed to be getting younger. Back in the day, it was the O.G.s that were on top and in control. But gradually, they either retired, went legit, got locked up, or were killed; leaving the streets wide open for the hungry up-and-comers.

Out of the many different names I'd heard, one echoed the loudest and the deadliest: Jackpot! It was rumored he got the name as a young stick-up-kid, when he literally hit the "jackpot" on a lick for a few million dollars and some bricks. But before he popped up on the scene, no one had known or heard of him. He just came out of nowhere and hit the streets hard, like an earthquake. Within a few months, he'd completely taken over the game.

Many thought Jackpot was black, because of his dark skin tone; but he was really Brazilian and brought a small team with him that the urban jungle seemed to be no challenge for. He came to take over by any means necessary. The murders of his competition and intimidation tactics were proof. He catapulted himself to the top of the streets, and there he stood, virtually unchallenged.

For now!

CHAPTER 46

1994 …

During my last few months, I started sending word to the streets for the Mob to start infiltrating Jackpot's organization: "Get in good and work for him or his team … Do whatever it takes," I advised in one of my kites to the streets.

Kendra wrote me from time to time, keeping me posted on everything. Then, I received the news I was waiting for: "Jackpot's been puttin' niggas on from the Mob," she informed me. Ever since I'd first heard about the nigga and the position he'd acquired in the streets, I'd planned on taking it over. So now that he was working with the Mob, my plan was in motion. He was a problem, one that a common approach wouldn't solve. A problem of his magnitude surely wouldn't be solved without bullets and bloodshed!

The last letter I'd received from Kendra informed me of a situation that bothered me even more than the Jackpot situation: "Hardball burned the bridge with Pelón. Primo didn't make it," she said.

"Fuck!" I yelled out so loud, the whole County Jail heard it. *This was not good. I introduced*

*Hardball to Pelón, so in his eyes I would be to blame!
I don't know how I'ma do it, but I gotta figure out
how to fix this!* I thought.

$$$$$

I was fresh out, and my recent stint in the County had
provided me plenty of time to reflect on my past, as
well as plot on my future. I was increasingly aware
of where I was and where I wanted to be. I was 21
now, a grown-ass man. It was time for me to step
back into the streets and fill the void that I'd created
by taking Kaydah's soul. The instant I took that Mob
chain off his neck and put it around mine, I accepted
the responsibilities that came with it. I'll be damned
if I don't represent the Mob like a real Boss is
supposed to. It was time to take over the streets once
and for all.

I was young, black, and free, with nothing to lose
and everything to gain. There was nothing more
dangerous that that combination. I was definitely up
against unfavorable odds. But, I was still able to find
an opportunity in even the most unfavorable of
situations. I was grinning, because the fire within was
creating an appetite; I was thirsty for blood and ready
to eat.

But first, I would need to call a Mob meeting and
learn all I could about Jackpot and his organization. I
also needed to know how deep the Mob's roots were
in his operation. Whatever roles the Mob played,
were definitely about to blow up in his face. In my
mind, the war that was about to spark up was a chess
game. One that would be won by thinking three or

four moves ahead at all times. I would be calculating moves with the whole Mob; most on my side of the board, and some strategically placed on his. Ya see, what Jackpot didn't realize was, them streets were my chessboard. He fucked up the second he allowed some of my chess pieces on this team. Which put the Mob in a position to win before the game even began. Check!

CHAPTER 47

I went straight to Kendra's, stepped in like I owned the place, and demanded my Mob chain.

After the detective had read me my rights, my momma had showed up at the hospital to check on me. I had her take the chain off my neck and made it clear that she had to take it straight to Kendra. I knew she would take care of it, and guard it with her life.

"Damn, nigga! No hello, how you been, I miss you … Nothing?" she asked, irritably.

"My bad, my nigga, you're right. I just ain't felt right since it came of my neck," I admitted.

"I feel you, bruh, real talk. But you're gonna give me a mu'fuckin' hug, nigga," she demanded.

I gave her a long hug, and held her tight: "There; now go get my damn chain," I smiled as I spoke.

"'Ight, 'ight, damn!" she shook her head as she disappeared to go get it.

Anticipation built as I waited to put the Mob chain back around my neck where it belonged. My heart rate seemed to increase by the second. It wasn't just excitement, it was the reality that came with it; I go from Paperboy, to Mob Boss! And with that position of power comes great responsibility.

"Welcome home, Mob!" Kendra said, interrupting my thoughts.

I looked up, and the sight of the Mob pendant dangling from her fist took my breath away! The dim light in the living room made the diamonds twinkle like stars in the night. Before I could even reach out to grab it, Kendra opened the chain with both hands, revealing a hole for me to put my head through. I did, and she draped it around my neck. I naturally stood a little taller and lifted my head with pride. It was like the power that came with wearing it, started flowing through my body. It was great to be home!

I had a whole kingdom to take over and needed to call a meeting: "Look, I need you to let the Mob know I'm home, and that we're gathering tonight at your spot for a very important meeting. Strictly Mob, no outsiders!" I explained to Kendra.

"Fa' sho', Mob, I'm on it."

"It's important that everybody is there," I stressed.

"Don't trip! I got it!" she nodded her head as she spoke.

"Ten sharp."

"Say no more," she ended the conversation.

I'd begun to leave, but stopped at the door. Before I could even get a word out my mouth, Kendra put her hand up as if to say "Stop!" Then, she reached between her couch cushions and came out with a 9mm Baretta.

"What, you're a mind reader or somethin'?" I joked.

"Naw, Mob, I just ain't new to this, I'm true to this," she responded as she handed it over.

"One in the neck?" I asked. The look she gave was the only answer I needed. "Well, I'ma need a ride!"

CHAPTER 48

I had Kendra drop me off at my spot in Parkside, so I could get ready and get my mind right for tonight's meeting. Since Kaydah was gone, I had my nigga Rydah from the Mob looking after the place. Bruh was another one of my brothers from the Lo, and he reminded me a lot of myself. I knew he was a nigga I could trust to take care of my spot, and keep everything in order while I was gone. Right after I linked up with Pelón, he was also a part of the first ten niggas I'd put on with a kick.

After I'd gotten locked up, bruh still owed me some money from a drop. So, I had him use it to pay the bills until I got out. Anything left over, I agreed was his to keep. One thing I didn't do, though, was tell him or anybody else about the secret room behind my closet wall. After the situation with Kaydah, I'd learned my lesson. All I did was tell my momma that if I ever died, to burn the place down, and there would be a surprise waiting for her in the ashes. The big-ass safe was fireproof. I also asked her, "You remember G-Ma's birthday, right?"

"Yeah, of course I do. She's my mom!" she retorted.

"Good! Don't forget it!" I demanded.

She looked confused, but she said, "OK."

I walked into my spacious three-bedroom spot, and grabbed a seat in my leather La-Z-Boy recliner. Then, I lifted the arm rest, which revealed the little compartment under it. Sure enough, there was a zip of White Widow and some swishers right where I'd left it. The weed was probably stale as fuck, but it was going to have to work for now.

I rolled up a fat bat, put it to my lips, and sparked the lighter. Just as I was filling my lungs full of smoke, I heard a noise coming from inside the house. *What the fuck?* I thought, as I snatched up the 9mm and listened closer. I could hear a commotion coming from one of my back bedrooms, and my killer instincts kicked in; like a shark that had smelled blood.

I made sure the banger was off safety and started creepin' towards the back. As I got closer, I pinpointed the guest bedroom as the source of where the noises were coming from. The door was closed, so I stepped back and booted it wide open! With my gun in hand and ready to shoot, I stepped in with two targets in my line of fire.

CHAPTER 49

The sound of Rydah's balls smacking against some bitch's pussy filled the air. His chain was bouncing off his bare chest as he continued to beat it up, even while I was pointing my gun at him! I chuckled and lowered my gun. The crazy nigga never even broke stride when I busted in. And the bitch was so busy getting' her back blew-out, she didn't even know I was there until Rydah said: "Welcome home, Mob! Come get you some of this."

The bitch finally lifted her face off the mattress and looked my way. She smiled, licked her lips, and waved a hand for me to come over. *Fuck it! I might as well*, I thought, as I walked over to the edge of the bed, stopping right in front of her face.

I whipped out and she took my limp dick into her mouth, sucking it right to life. While I was enjoying her face-time, I was thinking about the conversation me and this wild-ass nigga need to have. I'd asked him to pay the bills and feed the pits, not bring his hood-rats through. But I'd get to that later, after we finished running the bitch.

After we tag-teamed her and she swallowed my seeds, I pulled my pants up and dipped out to my living room. Then, I fired the blunt back up. I was halfway done with it, when Rydah came out buttoning his jeans up.

"What's good, Mob? I didn't think you'd be home for another week or two," Rydah said, as he walked over and grabbed a seat on the couch.

I remained silent, and just kept hitting my blunt. He knew I was hot and tried to make light of the situation.

"Did you see the ass on that bitch?" he asked, as he nudged his head in the direction of the bedroom.

Before I could even say anything, the Mexican bitch walked out, still naked. All she had on was some red pumps, and they had her voluptuous ass cheeks shifting sides with each step. She didn't have a care in the world, as if she was fully dressed, and that had both of us in a trance. Our eyes were glued on her ass; it was so big, you could literally sit a cup on it.

"Hey, Papi," she said, as she looked over at me and then she turned to Rydah: "So, was he a surprise, or did you not know he was coming over?" she asked him.

I couldn't believe my ears. Bruh was frontin' for the bitch, acting like my crib was his. Rydah looked at me, reading my mind. He just grinned and shrugged his shoulders as if to say: "Can you blame a nigga? Look at that ass!"

I was hot, but wasn't going to put my nigga on blast. So, I bounced up and motioned for him to follow me as I headed for the back door. Once out back, I spoke: "Bruh, what you doin' bringin' bitches through my spot?" I asked him with my face expressing anger. Then, I flashed a big-ass grin: "Baby does have tremendo' ass, though!" I said, as I stuck my fist out to give him some dap.

Rydah started laughing as we exchanged daps. "On the Mob, she do!" he said, agreeing.

"Just don't do no shit like that again, bruh, you know how I be when it comes to my spot," I said, sternly.

"You're right, bruh. That's my bad. My word, it won't happen again," he apologized.

"It's all good! But y'all gotta go. Oh, yeah, be at Kendra's tonight at ten; we're having a meetin'," I informed him.

"Fa' sho', I'll be there, and welcome home, Mob! The streets ain't been the same wit'out you," he expressed.

"Yeah, well, all that's about to change."

CHAPTER 50

Since I'd crashed the 5.0 after the shootout, I was gonna need some wheels to get around, and only had one option: the Coug-nut Kaydah had given me! When I'd initially parked it, I wasn't sure if I'd ever drive it again. But now, even though it was my only option, I was actually excited to pull it out the garage. I got in the driver's seat, pumped the gas pedal a few times, and turned the key. To my surprise, it started right up!

$$$$$

It was a little after ten when I pulled up to Kendra's and peeped a crowd of thugs posted up outside, hella deep. The Mob was ready to celebrate and welcome me home. It was a sight to see! We'd celebrate, alright, right after we killed Jackpot. As always, business before pleasure.

I hopped out the whip and was greeted with cheers and handshakes. I figured I was missed, but feeling that love meant the world to a nigga fresh out. Sometimes while locked up, we can't help but feel forgotten. It's that whole outta-sight-outta-mind feeling. But the fact is, when thugs are caught up in that fast life, they rarely get around to writing a letter. It's not personal, it's reality, and the love I was receiving was proof!

The Mob entered Kendra's spot and everyone gathered around the living room and dining room, which occupied the same floor space. It was loud, as everyone was bullshitting about this and that. I needed everyone's attention, so I grabbed it! I stood up on the couch in the corner of the living room and pulled my shirt off, which revealed the Mob chain. Almost instantly, the whole room got quiet.

"Mob! As y'all know, I called everyone here tonight for a meeting. Most, if not all of you, should already have an idea of what the context of this meeting will be. But before we get into all that, I would like for us to take a moment of silence and pay our respects to those who'd represented this chain before me. As well as to the many soldiers the Mob lost to this vicious game over the years! We need to channel them and their energies as we begin our next chapter. They're the gods that watch over us, and we're going to need 'em to guide us through the storm that's ahead of us. That moment of silence begins now!" A solid minute of silence ensued before I started again: "OK, Mob! The journey we're about to embark on, isn't nothin' we're not already accustomed to. We're just finna take it to a whole new level. We're all family in this room, you feel me? We came up together, struggled together, ate together, and we're finna move together at all times – as one Mob!" I paused for a second to let that sink in, and then I continued: "As y'all know, these are our streets. We're supposed to run these streets. But on some real shit, we slipped up and lost these streets to Jackpot! While I was knocking my time down, that nigga's name started ringin' like a trap phone. Which is why I started plottin' and sending kites for y'all to wiggle yo' way into his operation. Now, if you ain't caught on yet. I called this Mob meeting because we're 'bout to re-claim what's rightfully ours."

CHAPTER 51

Immediately, chatter picked up as the Mob conversated eagerly about the situation I'd laid before them. Of course, they were with it; no hood in America would be OK with an outsider running their streets. They just lacked the guidance needed to secure the territory. With Kaydah's death and all, I was mostly to blame for that, because Kaydah never would've allowed it to happen. But now that I'm home, I had to pick up the slack and put the streets back in order!

In the Mob, everyone has a role and something they're good at. Some are D-Boys, while others are killa's. Some are stick-up kids, while others are pimps. Some are jack-of-all-trades, and can flourish in any role. But, not everyone is a leader.

Me, I was bred to be a leader, by a leader. Not only was I a jack-of-all-trades, but I also possessed a natural leadership quality that's hard to find. Kaydah spotted it in me when I was young, and nurtured it, as well as myself, to peak potential. By doing so, he primed me for this exact moment. My role as leader of the Mob would soon be solidified with bloodshed, as I executed my plot to eliminate Jackpot and take back our streets. Once that's complete, I'll begin laying the foundation to our Empire.

"Everything that Jackpot built, and every dollar he's put in his pockets, belongs to us!" I said, as I looked around the room, making sure I had everyone's attention. "We're going to kill that nigga and anybody rockin' wit' him. The key to our success is going to be in our plot, and the strategic execution of that plot. In the Mob, we're always plottin' our next move, but a plot that worked yesterday, may not work for tomorrow's objective. It's about adapting to the situation at hand. Now, plottin' your next move involves a procedure and requires you to answer several fundamental questions. I'ma break all this down as we iron out the wrinkles, which may take a few days. After the plot is established, we'll move to the execution. So, for the next week, we'll be vigorously dissecting Jackpot's organization and figuring out his every move," I explained.

As a Mob Boss, I have to weigh my options carefully, because one wrong move could prove detrimental and get members of the Mob killed or worse – end the Mob altogether! That's why I had to educate the Mob and break everything down into a tried and proven science. The fate of the Mob was in my hands, and I'd be accountable for our actions and for the reactions they may cause. It's cause and effect; every action has a reaction, that's why I have to stress the importance of decision-making and make sure the strategies I'm teaching are implemented properly.

"The focus of our meetings over the next week will be to gather useful information and then use it to locate a vison. Then, I'll break down the process that'll allow us as a whole, to reach that vision. That process will give us a step-by-step path needed to make that vision a reality. Remember, 'knowledge is power,' and because y'all have been operating within Jackpot's organization, y'all possess the knowledge that will give us all the power we need." I paused, to let that sink in for a second: "Now, we already have an ace up our sleeve, because we've penetrated his operation. But, we also have the element of surprise, because he has no idea we're plottin' this takeover. So, I'ma need to know EVERYTHING the Mob knows about Jackpot and his organization. Let's get started."

CHAPTER 52

"Okay, before we get to the information on Jackpot, I'ma start by asking this question: How do we get to our goal from here? This question is important, because we're beginning with the end in mind. Can anybody answer that question?" I asked, to see if anybody's paying attention.

"That's easy, Mob. We plot it out like you've been talking about!" Jacka spat out, jumping right in.

"Exactly! Creating a plot takes four forms: Strategic, Tactical, Operational, and Contingency. Let me break these down for y'all, so we can utilize them while we gather info: Strategic, determines the main goals and the policies, procedures, strategies, and resources we'll need to achieve them; Policies, are our guidelines for action. Who can give me an example of a Mob policy?" I asked.

"Shoot first and ask questions later!" Teardrop shouted out.

"Facts! Strategies, determine the best way to use our resources. Who can give me an example of the Mob's resources?" I asked.

159

"Money, whips, guns, and soldiers!" Rydah answered.

"Indeed! During the strategic phase, we'll decide which opps to take out first, where to find them, at what times, and who will take them on. Any questions?" I asked.

No one spoke, so I continued: "Now, to Tactical! This is the process of developing detailed short-term objectives of what needs to be done, who is to do it, and how such plans can include setting dates and places, and deciding on other activities necessary to meet strategic objectives. Y'all got that?"

Everyone nodded their understanding.

"Okay, good! So, Operational. This is basically setting weapon standards like, 'AK-47s' or 'handguns', and creating schedules to implement our tactical objectives. Understood?"

Again, everyone nodded.

"Last, but not least, Contingency, which is the process of preparing alternative courses of action we'd use if primary plans don't work out. Can anybody give me an example of this?"

"If the opp we're targeting isn't there; then, we'll have another opp that we know to go and take out," Jacka answered, staying involved.

"Exactly! Situations can change rapidly, so it's wise to have alternative plans of action ready in anticipation of such changes. But, sometimes we have to make decision on the spot. The key is to make good decisions in the circumstances. That means having good judgment and acting fast." This time, as I looked around, everybody was already nodding.

It was time to move on and figure out everything the Mob knew about Jackpot and his organization.

CHAPTER 53

"Okay, Mob. Now that y'all understand the four forms of creating a plot, we're going to move on. These next questions are intended for the Mob members working within Jackpot's organization. If in any shape, form, or fashion you've been a part of his operation, come to the front of the room. If not, move to the back!" I directed.

The room began to shift. Once everyone was in place, I started again: "I'ma throw out some questions and I want y'all to think about the answers for a second before you respond: What are the opps' success factors in the streets, and how do we compare?" I ask the Mob members in the front row. A few seconds passed before anyone answered.

"They don't hesitate to kill anybody in their way," one Mob member explained.

"That's definitely one of their success factors, but it's nothing we can't handle; we have killa's as well. Anything else?" I persisted.

"They seem to have an unlimited supply of coke," another suggested.

"I got you! We'll need a plug, that's for sure, but I got that covered," I said, hoping my plan to smooth things over with Pelón would work. "Anything else?" I asked.

No one spoke, so I continued: "What seems to be Jackpot and his goons' state of mind, or thought process?" I asked. Again, a few seconds passed before anyone spoke.

"They think they're untouchable. That no one is stupid enough to try them," a Mob member from the back group chimed in.

"You obviously aren't a part of their operation. So, how do you know that?" I quizzed.

"'Cause I was at the shop gettin' my shit cut, while two of Jackpot's goons were there also. They were super cocky, talking out loud and literally saying exactly that. Basically, bragging!" he said.

"Okay, that's good to know. That means they're slippin'. If they think nobody will try them, then they won't be ready for an ambush," I explained. Then I continued: "Who are Jackpot's major shooters? They'll be who we take out first."

"I already have that figured out," Kendra said.

"Let me hear it," I said, encouraging her to continue.

"Once you started sending word for us to infiltrate jackpot's organization, I started paying close attention and keeping tabs on his goons. Each of his main shooters run a different trap. They supply the trap houses, and collect money every Friday at noon, like clockwork," Kendra announced proudly.

"Well, that answers that and my next question; what opportunities exist for us to catch them slippin'?

Now that we know that, we'll hit every single trap house at the same time, Friday at noon. By doing so we'll kill two birds wit' one stone; kill his goons and rob them niggas," I decided, as the plan was coming together perfectly.

I was thankful that Kendra had been doing her homework and was able to figure out that part of their operation. Now, I just hoped somebody would have the answer to my next question: "There's one more critical question that we'll need the answer to before we can put our plot in motion. Where does Jackpot lay his head?" I asked, scanning the room.

CHAPTER 54

"I don't know exactly where, but I know he stays up in Concord. He used to fuck wit' my ex-bitch Unique. She owns the beauty shop downtown. But now, he fucks wit' Unique's cousin, so she has a sour taste in her mouth and stays volunteering info on the nigga," Kendra said eagerly, ready and willing to knock the nigga Jackpot down with me.

"So, you know this bitch Unique personally?" I asked.

"Yeah! The bitch is low-key bi-sexual and we've been fuckin' around from time to time for years," she boasted, while nodding her head." You know who she is, Paper; she's the one who used to swoop me on the block in the 5.0."

"Oh, fa' sho'! This nigga is already in check and don't even know it," I said, referencing a chess game and meaning every word: "Well, go eat that bitch pussy real good tonight, and get her to drop the location on Jackpot," I instructed.

"I got it, don't even trip!" she said, confidently.

"I swear, bitches are always a nigga's downfall."
I started laughing as I thought out loud.

$$$$$

Before the end of the week, Kendra had Jackpot's location, and we had our takeover plot completely ironed out; as smooth as could be. The tactical plot consisted of six teams in total. Five, to hit all five traps Jackpot's goons were running, and the other to hit Jackpot himself. It was a green light for the following Friday at noon, when they did their drop/pickup.

Each of the five teams had a known shooter as its squad leader. This was important, because as the hit unfolded, it could get chaotic; so we wanted experienced shooters to command authority. Each squad leader has three additional Mob members behind him: one to drive, one to get the drugs, and one to get the money. The whole team will hit each trap, guns blazin'. After the shooting dies down, the squad leader will keep lookout while the driver gets the whip and the other two get the dope and money. The contingency was, if anybody got killed, roles changed; and everybody knew each variation, right down to if only one Mob member survived.

I led the sixth team that would be hitting Jackpot. But, our tactical plot was a little different. Since Jackpot was tucked off in an up-scale neighborhood and not in the hood; we would hit him as stealthily as possible. Which, for one thing, meant guns with silencers. I had only two Mob members with me; Kendra and Jacka.

We stole an all-white soccer-mom van, and dipped out to Concord. We bent the corner down Jackpot's street.

"There it is," Kendra pointed to a white-colored house with blue trim.

The house wasn't too large, but it was definitely nice and extremely expensive. I parked the soccer-mom van in the street, right in front of the house. The street was quiet and deserted, in a neighborhood where 'noon' meant everyone was just going to lunch, at whatever company they worked for. With all the info Kendra got from Unique, we learned that Jackpot liked to keep a low profile, and lived discreetly. That way, he could come and go virtually unnoticed by neighbors. No goons, no sore-thumb whips or loud music; just him and his bitch.

We had the van disguised as a pizza delivery vehicle, with a "Pizza Hut" light on the roof. To go with it, I was dressed as a pizza delivery guy. I had a Pizza Hut uniform that included the shirt and hat. It was one of the many different uniforms that we kept handy, which included everything from construction worker, to police uniforms. I was carrying a pizza delivery heat bag. It was the decoy that would get them to open the door. Instead of a pizza being inside, I had a nine-milli' with a silencer, locked and loaded.

Kendra and Jacka stayed out of sight on both sides of the door, while I rang the doorbell: Ding! Dong!

CHAPTER 55

No one came!

I rang it again, this time twice: Ding! Dong! Ding! Dong! Then, the sounds of footsteps coming down stairs let me know it was go-time!

"Who is it?" some bitch asked, pushing the door curtain aside to peek out the glass design at the top.

"Pizza delivery," I said, holding up the heat bag with the Pizza Hut logo on top.

"We're not expecting any pizza?" her face contorted in confusion. Once she said "we're" I knew Jackpot was there: "It was actually paid for already with a credit card. Can you check the receipt and see if you recognize the name?" I asked, holding up a random receipt I had for this purpose.

"It might be for one of the neighbors," she said, as she was unlocking the door.

She opened it, and I had the nine-milli' pointed right between her eyes: "Bitch, don't scream, don't yell, don't even fuckin' breathe," I demanded firmly.

Kendra and Jacka came around the door and snatched her up, telling her to keep quiet. I stepped into the living room where Kendra had the bitch in a choke hold, with her gun pointed at the bitch's temple.

"Where's he at?" I asked, with my gun still pointed at her head.

"He's upstairs sleeping. Last door on the right," she whispered, seemingly in shock.

I ran up the stairs quietly, taking two steps at a time. Jacka was right behind me. We arrived at the door, and it was left halfway open. I peeked in and seen the shape of a body under the covers, a loud snore growled from underneath. I flipped on the light and stood over his body with my gun pointed at his head. Then, I kicked the bed with force.

"What the fuck?" Jackpot barked as he sat up, with sleep still in his eyes. As he regained his vision, his eyes rested on the barrel. It was pointed so close to his face, he went cross-eyed: "Who the fuck are you niggas?" he roared, all 250 pounds of him raging. The bull inside him was kept at bay by the gun, though.

"You know what it is, nigga! Give me what I want, 'fore you get what you don't," I said, and I could see the motor in his mind spinning at breakneck speed. He was hoping for an opportunity to turn the tables: "Just tell us where the money and the dope is, and nobody has to die today," I lied, trying to get him to comply and expose where his stash was.

The nigga didn't feel the true gravity behind my words. Every muscle in his body flexed and pulsated with rage: "Who sent you? Do you niggas know who the fuck I am?" he seethed.

"Wrong answer!" I let off a round into his leg. Peew! "I'ma ask you one more time; where is the money and the dope?" I continued as Jackpot cringed and growled, trying his best not to appear hurt or scared.

"I ain't tellin' you niggas where shit is!" he said, full of pride.

I squeezed the trigger three times, hitting the nigga once in the chest and twice in the head. His body slumped on the bed as blood oozed from his mouth and his eyes stared into space. As I was searching the room, the smell of feces began to overpower the air. I didn't know that when someone died, their muscles relaxed, and frequently a last bowel movement ensued: "Checkmate! Bitch-ass nigga!" I said, declaring victory.

CHAPTER 56

"Search the house and see what you can find. I'ma go question the bitch and see what she knows, then I'ma dust her off, too," I told Jacka as I made my way down the stairs.

As I stepped back into the living room, the bitch obviously knew Jackpot was dead. She had fear written all over her face, but remained silent.

"I'm only going to ask you once; where does he keep the money and the dope?" I said, approaching with my gun pointed at her. Knowing I wasn't playing, Kendra moved out of the way.

"I don't know, but every now and then he would climb up into the attic. Maybe it's in there." She spoke through gasps of air, as her chest heaved up and down and her heart pounded.

Peew! Peew! I finished her off with a quiet two to the wig. Then, I pushed back up the stairs towards the attic door in the hallway. I pulled the string, lowered the door and folded out the ladder: "Aye, bruh, over here," I called out to Jacka as I started climbing into the attic.

Right in the middle of the floor was a chest. It looked like an old-school treasure chest: "Jackpot!" I yelled out loud, being funny, as Jacka was making his way in.

"The nigga can't be stupid enough to keep anything major at his spot?" Jacka wondered, seeing the chest as well.

"Help me get this big mu'fucka' down, so we can bust it open," I said to Jacka, knowing I'd need his help.

After we got the chest down, by literally dropping it out the attic, we carried it into the living room. It was definitely heavy: "Kendra, go in the garage and see what you can find to beat this open," I instructed.

She dipped off, and came back with a sledgehammer: "Watch out!" she warned, as she went to the chest and swung the hammer at the lock. Bang! She busted the master lock right off and opened the chest.

Our eyes widened with amazement as they rested on the colorful sparkle of jewelry that filled the chest. It looked like a real treasure chest, full of gold. There was all kinds of jewelry, both men's and women's. Everything from chains, pendants, bracelets, rings, earrings, and watches. Some of it had diamonds or other stones, and some of it didn't. Most likely, it was stolen by crackheads and traded to Jackpot's goons for rocks. The jewelry was probably worth a lot of money, but it definitely wasn't what we were looking for: "Let's finish searching the house," I said.

"I'll search the garage and the cars," Kendra volunteered.

"I'll finish searching upstairs," Jacka decided.

That left me to search downstairs.

We ransacked the rest of the house, and it turned up a duffel bag with a hunnid bands inside, a black garbage bag with about a pound of weed in it, some guns, some more jewelry, and a money counter. *That money counter is going to come in handy,* I thought, just as Kendra came back in from the garage.

"Aye, Paper! Check this shit out!" she said, holding up a Ziplock bag with a folded piece of paper and a key in it: "It's a contract to a storage unit in Antioch. It was in the glove box," she continued.

"Let me see! That's gotta be where he keeps everything!" I said with excitement in my voice: "That's a good find, Kendra! Let's go check it out!" I congratulated her.

We loaded everything we found in the house into the van, and headed to the storage in Antioch.

$$$$$

Just as I'd hoped, the storage unit was, in fact, where Jackpot stashed everything. There was what I guesstimated to be two-million dollars, about sixty bricks of coke, and a whole arsenal of weapons: "I was joking earlier, but we really did hit the jackpot!" I said, grinning from ear to ear.

Now that we found his stash spot, I needed to figure out our next move. I was thinking for a second, and then an idea hit me: "Kendra, do you got I.D. on you?" I asked her.

"Yeah! Why?" she asked, wondering what I had in mind.

"Go to the front and open a storage. We'll move all this shit right into it!" I told her and she shot me a look like I was crazy: "It's just for now! We'll open another one in a crackhead's name later," I continued, hoping to ease her worries.

"Fuck it! I'll be back," she agreed hesitantly.

CHAPTER 57

The trap houses were easy targets, because none of Jackpot's goons expected, nor were ready, to be hit. They were running their operation feeling untouchable, based strictly on their reputation. In their minds, everyone feared Jackpot and those who were in his organization. Most did, but the Mob didn't. And the hit was proof!

The other five squads hit each trap house at the same time, while we were hitting Jackpot. Each squad was parked inconspicuously down the street from the targeted trap house, lurkin'. They were instructed to wait until the "drop/pickup" was in motion. Kendra informed us that each car would pull into the garage, and it would be closed while the transaction was in motion. So, the orders were, as soon as the garage door closes, move in and kill anything breathing. Then, they would grab the money and the dope, before getting ghost! The agreement was that each squad would split up what they came up on and killed for.

By killing Jackpot and his goons, their whole organization was wiped out, and the legend of the Mob skyrocketed to a whole new level! Anybody else that was working within their organization, immediately went into hiding. Jackpot and his goons did a lot of damage, leaving nothing but blood and shell casings behind them. But now that they're out the way, the kingdom was back under the Mob's rule; and I had big plans! My heavy-handed approach was justified in the name of a victorious end. But, I still had one hurdle to overcome. The coke we came up on would run out soon enough, so I had to figure out how to make things right with Pelón.

$$$$$

I was home, and our plot to eliminate Jackpot and take back our streets was successful; it was time for a Mob celebration. We arrived at the club, and the line extended all the way down the block! It was ridiculous the amount of people that were waiting to get in. We stepped out of a trail of limo's and all eyes were on us as we bypassed the line. Once inside, we were escorted to our V.I.P. section by a thick-ass waitress that looked like she belonged on stage.

The bottle service was poppin'; there were buckets of ice with our favorite bottles in them. All around the section, the entire Mob was in attendance, which required us to reserve all the club's V.I.P. sections, and turn them into one!

"We have a special announcement to make on behalf of the Mob," the sound of the DJ's voice pumped out the speakers: "Welcome home, Paperboy." He and the entire Mob yelled in unison.

I was definitely caught off guard, and overwhelmed by all the love I was receiving. I was speechless, so I grabbed a bottle of champagne and popped the top; a stream of the alcohol shot into the air. That set off a domino effect and the whole Mob started poppin' bottles. We literally made it rain!

I stood smiling as I watched the Mob celebrate. The liquor was flowing as beautiful waitresses tended to us with bottle after bottle. All the baddest bitches in the building ornamented our section like jewels, and it was obvious their hormones were on fire. I couldn't help but feel invigorated, renewed, and free.

"We have a lil' surprise for you," Kendra spoke into my ear so I could hear over the noise.

"Oh, yeah? What is it?" I asked.

"Follow me!" she said, leading the way to a private dance booth.

"Now that's how you welcome a nigga home," I smiled, ready to enjoy my surprise.

"Have fun," Kendra said, leaving me to myself and my thoughts.

"I hope she's sexy as fuck!" I thought, while waiting to see who'd be giving me my private dance. A few seconds later, a beautiful brown-skinned Mexican female stepped in. She look exotic with her long hair and cat eyes. She had her hair pulled back into a pony-tail that hung down past her ass, and big hoop earrings on. Her plumpness had my full attention, until the light flashed across her face. My jaw dropped in surprise as I recognized the woman in front of me!

CHAPTER 58

"Hi, Paperboy," Abby said shyly, once she knew I'd finally recognized her.

She had a frame that was thicker than I'd remembered; her titties were as plump as melons, and she had an ass so fat, that it shifted with every stride. Her full lips and cat-shaped eyes gave her the look of an Egyptian goddess.

"Surprise," she smiled, as I was admiring her stunning beauty.

Thinking about it now, I do remember hearing that she'd started stripping: "Surprise is right!" I said, reaching out and grabbing her hand. I pulled her towards me and she hopped on my lap and started kissing me; exactly as she did all them years ago, when I snatched her from that nigga Messy Marv.

"I've missed you, Papi," she whispered.

"I can't lie, I've missed yo' sexy ass, too," I admitted.

She began grinding her hot twat into my crotch as she was kissing me passionately. My crotch immediately responded and began to stiffen as I grabbed her fat ass cheeks, which were melting between my fingers.

"Put those pretty lips to work for me, ma!" I said, with a tone of authority that didn't leave her any room to object.

She backed off my lap, dropped to her knees and leaned into my lap. She unzipped my pants with her teeth as she worked my belt with her hands. After there was nothing left in the way, she pulled out my throbbing pole. She was holding my long thickness in her manicured hand and she licked the head of my pipe, and started circling it seductively around my tip. My manhood jumped from excitement.

"Oh, shit! I groaned, as I put my hand on the back of her head. I grabbed her ponytail and gently pushed her down on me.

She took all of me into her throat, gagging a little from my size. Her mouth was wet and warm, and I was in heaven as I watched her sexy face intent on pleasing me. She slobbered on my pole as she deep-throated every inch. She knew she was nice with her tongue as she worked her skills with confidence.

Not even five minutes had passed, and I felt the swell of the last nine months nearing ejaculation. I closed my eyes, and she slid her mouth up and down with precision, tickling the vein underneath my shaft while doing so. It was a wrap; my dick went into convulsions and I unloaded everything deep into her throat.

"Damn, baby! What time you get off? I'm tryna hit that pussy till the sun comes up, like old times," I said, while pushing her thong to the side and massaging her swollen clit.

She began to moan as I fingered her dripping insides. I was working my fingers in and out of her like a dick: "My shift just ended," she moaned into my ear.

CHAPTER 59

I hopped out of Abby's car and walked around to the passenger side, opening the door for her.

"Thanks, baby," she stated with a smile. Then she grabbed my hand and arm, pulling herself close to me as we walked. We got to her front door, she unlocked it, and we went in.

"I need to take a piss. I'll be right out," I said, as the door shut.

I handled my business, washed my hands, and made my way towards her bedroom. When I walked in, I seen her laying in the bed completely naked, with her four-inch stilettos still on. I paused and admired the curves of her body; her round, heavy titties, flat stomach, and apple-shaped bottom gave me an instant hard-on. I'd missed the treasure that she had between her legs, and couldn't wait to slide inside her again.

"Okay, sexy. I see you still know how to excite a nigga," I said, getting harder, dick bulging in my jeans.

"I guess so!" she said with a smile, while looking at the tent in my jeans.

I took off my shirt, exposing muscle and tattoos, and lay in the bed next to her. She climbed on top of me and left a trail of kisses from my ear, to my chest, and she continued to move south. She got to my pants, unbuckled my belt, and worked my pants completely off. Then, she pulled my boxers off as well, and lay down between my legs.

She took my rock-hard rod into her mouth, and started masturbating my length as she sucked it. She was using her other hand to lightly massage my balls. The combination felt amazing and in no time I could feel my nut building up. I wasn't ready to bust yet, so I had to force myself to ease out of her mouth. Her head-game had always been superb, but her sex-game was even better.

"I want some of that pussy, baby," I said, sinking my extended-gold fangs into my bottom lip.

She climbed on top and laid my hardness down to my belly button. Then, she straddled it so that her fat-pussy lips parted around my pole. She started sliding forward and backwards on my undercarriage. I could feel her moistness as she started sliding back and forth even faster. Her wetness began to drip onto my lap, and it only added to the mind-blowing experience. I felt my nut building up again, and I grabbed her waist, slowing her down as I helped her slide back and forth; I was pushing her all the way to my balls and then pulling her all the way to my tip, nice and slow!

I knew I would release at any second, so I stopped fighting it. I lay all the way back, and she sped back up. At that point, there was nothing I could do, but explode an enormous load all over my stomach. After I was done, she lapped it all up, licking me clean.

The experience amazed me, because it was the first time a female used her coochie to make me cum without my dick actually entering her!

It was only 2 a.m., and sunrise was about four hours away; we were just getting started!

CHAPTER 60

I was fresh out and knew I would need some time to recuperate after that nut. So, I pulled Abby down next to me and started kissing on her neck passionately. Each kiss was wet, with just enough suction that I wasn't giving her a hicky. I continued down with the kisses, focusing on her erotic spots. I knew the more I explored her body with foreplay, the wetter she became.

My kisses finally landed on her pulsating clit, and she let out a soft moan that made the blood rush back into my cock. I was stimulating her clit by sucking and licking it with force. Then, I lowered my tongue and dipped it right into her puddle. Doing so caused her moans to get louder. It seemed the louder her moans got, the harder my dick got. But I was in no rush to get between her legs; I wanted to bring her to an orgasm with my tongue first.

Once her moans turned into screams, I inserted two fingers into her wetness. I was driving them in and out of her rapidly, while also working my tongue around her clit. The combination did its trick and brought her to a powerful climax. Now, I was ready for the sexual marathon I had planned.

By the time daylight crept though the curtains, we'd fucked in every position we could possibly think of and were completely satisfied. The night had flown by, but our reunion definitely made up for lost time. I was home and it felt good. Real good!

$$$$$

Abby dropped me off at home, and I had one thing, and one thing only, on my mind: "How am I going to smooth things out with Pelón?" I had a plan, but there was no guarantee it would work. Shit, he probably wanted to kill me. With this dilemma weighing heavily on my mind, I turned on some music and started rolling a blunt.

The sound of Pac serenaded the air, as I was filling my lungs with weed smoke. Pac was more than just a rapper; he was a street novelist, a poet! Smoking a blunt and listening to Pac, was like therapy. It was easy for me to get lost in the reality of his lyrics, and zone out! I was halfway through my blunt, when I heard a loud "slap" against my door.

"What the fuck," I said out loud, as I grabbed my heat and looked out the window. I seen the paperboy riding his bike down the street, throwing papers at the neighbors' front doors. *I remember them days*, I thought, as I went to grab my newspaper.

I picked it up and read the headline: "Kingpin Drug Lord Murdered," was splashed across the front page.

CHAPTER 61

Most thugs are impulsive, while I'm a thinker. I plan every move before I make it. So, I made sure I had all my ducks in a row, before I called Pelón.

"Amigo, I heard what happened, and I would like to sit down with you for a conversation," I said, getting straight to the point.

"Sí, Paperboy. I think a conversation would be bueno. Meet me in one hour, and come alone," he agreed.

"I'll be there."

I pulled up to the same designated spot, where we always did our business. This time, I didn't park in the front like I usually did; instead, I drove around to the back of the property and parked there.

Pelón came out the back door with two Mexicans behind him, both holding AK-47s: "Fuck! I hope this works," I said to myself, as I tucked my nickel-plated .45 on my waist and hopped out.

"Come in, amigo, and we talk," Pelón barked with the usual authority in his voice.

I didn't respond, just made my way in and sat in the exact spot I was sitting when we had our first conversation and established our business relationship. Pelón also took his seat and the two Mexicans stood guard off to the side.

"First off, I would like to apologize for what happened to Primo. I hope you know I had nothing to do with that!" I said, sparking the conversation.

"Amigo, you brought Hardball to me to do business, now my Primo is dead. That blood is on your hands!" he spat, with a cold stare.

"All I did was make an introduction. The choice was yours to do business with Hardball or not. You chose to do business with him; that's not on me!" I spat back, with a cold stare of my own.

"So, you're saying it's my fault my Primo is dead?" he asked, raising his voice and turning crimson red.

"No, amigo, it's Hardball's fault Primo is dead; not mine and not yours! I understand that I introduced him to you, so for that I would like to make it right!" I stated.

"Make it right? How do you plan on doing that?" he asked, confused and irritated.

"All I can do, amigo, is repay you for your loss! Follow me." I got up and started walking towards the back door. The two Mexicans raised their chops and stopped me dead in my tracks.

"You think money can fix this?" Pelón asked.

"Amigo, first let me show you. Then, you let me know if it's enough to make it right!" I stated simply.

He waved off the Mexicans, and nodded for me to continue. Then, he followed me to my trunk.

"This is the best I can do, amigo!" I said as I popped the trunk and took a step back.

CHAPTER 62

Pelón wasn't prepared for what was before him. His eyes got wide as he focused on the inside of the trunk. What he saw totally took him by surprise. It was a man, hog-tied, with his mouth duct-taped shut. Pelón stepped back in confusion.

"Don't step back, look closer! A life for a life is my repayment, amigo!" I stated calmly as I stepped to the side, giving him a better view.

He hesitatingly stepped forward and realized the man was Hardball, the man who'd killed his Primo. Hardball started to squirm, trying desperately to release himself from the bondage. Then, a smile spread across Pelón's face.

"I introduced him to you, so it's only right that I bring him to you so you can avenge your Primo's death," I told Pelón, as I pulled the .45 from my waist: "An eye for an eye! Do you wanna kill him, or do you want me to do it?" I asked, allowing him the option.

$$$$$

"Kendra, I need you to find Hardball and bring him to me, alive!" I said, hoping she'd be able to find the nigga.

"Hardball? I know a club he frequents in the city; I'll see if I can catch him there," she replied.

"Take a few niggas, and even a set-up bitch, whatever works! Just snatch that nigga up. Can you handle that?" I asked.

"Yeah, I got it, Mob!" she replied with confidence.

"As soon as you have that nigga, call me!" I demanded.

"It's good. I'm on it."

I knew the only way Pelón would even consider fucking with me again, was if I brought him the nigga that robbed and killed his Primo! So that was the plan.

"We got him, Mob. What now?" Kendra asked.

"Make the nigga take you to his dope and money. Beat him 'til he gives you the location if you have to, just don't kill him! Then, bring him and everything else to me," I replied, figuring we might as well rob him while we're at it.

"Say no more!" She hung up.

$$$$$

Pelón took the gun, examined it, then focused back on Hardball, who had the fear of death in his eyes. His muffled pleas fell on deaf ears, while Pelón anticipated revenging his Primo's death. He pointed the gun right at Hardball's top.

"Hold up," I said, reaching in and grabbing the two duffel bags stuffed in the back of the trunk, one full of money, the other full of dope. Then, I nodded my head so Pelón could handle his business.

Without hesitation he put two rounds into Hardball's skull. Then, he handed the gun back to me, and I emptied the rest of the clip into the lifeless body.

"This is everything he had when we snatched him up," I said, pointing to the two duffels.

"Keep it! I appreciate your honorable gesture," Pelón expressed, as he extended his hand with gratitude.

We locked hands and eyes, sealing a new bond.

"Our conversation isn't over yet, amigo, we still have one problem to figure out. Come inside!" he stated, before releasing his grip.

CHAPTER 63

We stepped back inside and returned to our prior positions at the table; the two Mexicans resumed their position as well.

"I believe you killed one of mi amigos," Pelón stated, rather than asking.

"What? Who?" I asked, confused.

"Jackpot!" he stated, looking directly in my eyes.

I just matched his stare without a blink. I was caught completely off guard, and my pistol was empty. All I could do was wonder where he was going with this conversation.

"You see, this is a problem for me, amigo. Jackpot was grabbing one-hundred kilos at a time, and that's a lot of money my pockets are missing now because of you!" he proceeded while we continued our staring contest.

"I hear what you're saying, amigo, but that's not a problem!" I retorted with confidence.

"No? Why is that not a problem?" he asked, lifting an eyebrow.

"'Cause the streets Jackpot was running his operation on belong to the Mob. They belong to me and my people, so he had to go. Now that he's no longer in the way, I'll be the one grabbing a hundred kilos at a time!" I rationalized, solving his problem and mine.

"I had a feeling you would say that, amigo. I love it when I'm right," he bragged with a smile: "You went above and beyond to prove your loyalty to me, amigo. For that, I'm going to open your eyes to a whole new world. Welcome to the big leagues, amigo!" he congratulated, as he got up from the table and disappeared into the kitchen.

It was déja-vu, as he emerged with the same bottle of tequila; the one with the worm in it, and two glasses with ice. He filled them both up, and picked his glass up, extending it to me. I picked up mine and extended it as well.

"To the big leagues, amigo!" Pelón said.

"To the big leagues!" I repeated as we connected our glasses, making a "clink" sound.

CHAPTER 64

Pelón said something in Spanish to the two Mexicans; they both nodded in my direction, and left.

"So, amigo, you're ready to grab one-hundred bricks, aye?" Pelón asked, pouring us both another glass.

"Ya' damn right! But first, we gotta talk prices, amigo," I responded in a true hustla's fashion.

"Of course, amigo. That's exactly what I wanted to talk to you about," he nodded as he spoke; "Before you got arrested, you were getting them for fifteen Gs, sí?" he continued, getting straight to business.

"Yeah! I was paying fifteen a kilo," I acknowledged.

"And you were grabbing twenty at a time, sí?" he asked, even though he knew.

"Exactly!" I again acknowledged.

"Well, amigo, now that you'll be grabbing five times that amount, I'd be willing to give them to you for ten Gs apiece," he said, throwing me a price.

Usually, I'd counter. But in this case, I knew ten Gs a kilo was a generous offer, and it was exactly the price I'd had in mind: "Ten Gs a kilo it is, amigo" I happily accepted, while doing the quick math in my head ($10,000 x 100 = 1 million dollars). "I'll have the mill' for you in the morning," I continued.

"Perfecto. Now, amigo, I must ask: How do you plan on transporting one hundred kilos?" he asked with a smirk.

"That's a good question. I was just trying to figure that out myself," I admitted with a chuckle.

"Like I said, amigo, this is the big leagues. What's your favorite sport?" he asked.

"Basketball," I responded.

"That lifestyle you're used to, is now your old way of life. You have a lot to learn, a lot to change, and a lot of people to meet, amigo!" he explained, piquing my interest.

"I'm listening, amigo, and I'm ready to learn," I assured him.

"Think of it like this, amigo; you started off playing street basketball, then you elevated to college hoops, and now you're in the N.B.A.! You're in the majors, and not too many have what it takes to get here, amigo!" He paused, letting that sink in, just as Kaydah used to. "But you made it, and now you have to learn a whole new playbook, amigo. I will teach you, amigo, I'm your coach. Comprende?" he continued, making perfect sense.

"I understand," I answered, doing more listening than talking.

"Okay, bueno. Now, amigo, we never move one hundred kilos in regular carro or truck. We trick the eye of the policia and move kilos in taxi, tow truck, company work van, U-Haul, or even a school bus.

Policia never expect that." He again paused, as the reality of his world was sinking in. "How many times you see a taxi or school bus pulled over, amigo?" he asked.

"Never," I admitted.

"Well, amigo, I'll see you here 7 a.m. I'll have the kilos and a ride for you to transport it," he said, finishing his glass.

"Seven a.m." I agreed, then I finished my glass as well.

CHAPTER 65

Beep! Beep! Beep! Beep!

I'd set my alarm for five a.m.! I stepped out of bed, stretched my arms wide, and looked out the window. The light of the sun was just peeking over the horizon. I'd always been an early-bird, a habit I acquired from Kaydah. "The early bird gets the worm; if you're really hungry, you'll be the first one on the block in the morning and the last one to leave at night," I remember him telling me during one of our first meetings.

Speaking of meetings, I had one with Pelón in exactly two hours. Pelón reminded me a lot of Kaydah. They both had that ambitions "Sky's the limit" type of drive, that was complemented by the wisdom of a boss that's been there and done it. Coming from a fatherless broken home, I've been fortunate to've found the role models I have in the streets. The game gods have definitely been watching down on me, because if it wasn't for Kaydah and Pelón, who knows where I'd be? Most likely, not in the big leagues!

I grabbed the duffel bag of money that the Mob came up on when they snatched up Hardball. Then I started flipping through the different denominations of bills as I diligently separated the ones, fives, tens, twenties, fifties, and hundreds. I started six different piles, one for each dollar amount. Once I was done separating the bills, I grabbed the money counter I'd gotten from Jackpot, and started running money through it. I knew it would come in handy, and was glad I didn't have to count all that money by hand!

I wrapped every ten bands with a rubber band and set it on the table. Altogether, there were four-hundred sixty bands in Hardball's duffel. *Good lookin' out, bruh*, I thought, as I went into my secret room to grab the other five-hundred forty bands. That was fifty-four more 10G stacks to make an even million. I put fifty of the ten-band stacks into an empty duffel, and the other four in the duffel that contained Hardball's money. There it was, two duffels containing a million dollars in total.

I contemplated smoking a blunt, but at that moment, I was high off life. Instead, I tucked the two duffels in my secret room and jumped in the shower. After I got out, I got dressed and headed out to meet Pelón for our next meeting, and to get my first hundred bricks.

CHAPTER 66

I pulled up slappin' and was about ten minutes early, so I decided to let the Pac song finish before I went in. I grabbed the two duffels and made my way to the front door. I felt my heart rate quicken from the excitement. As I was ascending the front steps to the porch, Pelón opened the door.

"Buenos días, amigo," he said, greeting me.

"A good morning it is," I agreed.

"Come in, amigo, would you like some coffee?" he offered.

"Naw, I'ma pass on the coffee. Good lookin' out, though," I respectfully declined.

I stepped into the dark living room, and as soon as my eyes adjusted, my heart dropped. Sitting right on the table was the one-hundred kilos. I'm talking about so much white, my eyes hurt. I'd never seen so many plastic-wrapped bricks before. Bricks so pure, the Mob could turn one into two and sell each one for an easy seventeen-five. That's a fast thirty-five Gs they could bring in by selling them whole. If they busted them down into zips, and sold each one for six-hundred, that amount inflates to over forty-three Gs.

When it comes to selling dope, I'm like a mathematician. I'm always working numbers and trying to figure out profit margins. Now that I'm getting the kilos for ten Gs apiece, I can drop them on the Mob for twenty Gs instead of thirty apiece, and I'd still be doubling my money. Just like that I could turn one million into two! I had definitely graduated into the big leagues, and it brought me a rush no drug could ever provide, one that's only created by a hustla's ambition.

"That's right, amigo, the big leagues!" he said, interrupting my thoughts.

I don't know if he was reading my mind, or if I was thinking out loud: "You a mind reader or something? Because that's exactly what I was thinking." I laughed.

"No, amigo. I've been where you are, and I had that same look in my eye," he admitted.

"Oh, okay. I was just checking. So where you want me to put the money?" I asked, feeling my arms getting tired from holding all that money.

"Let me see," he said, reaching his hands out.

I handed him the duffel bags and he set them down. Then he zipped them open and made a quick calculation of the ten-G-stacks. Then he zipped them back up and set them on the table next to the blow.

"Your ride should be here soon, amigo. This transport vehicle is a gift from me to you. But, I will set you up with my amigo from the Asian Mafia. That way, you can buy your workers some work vans with secret compartments for the product. Their safety is your safety, remember that!" he said, opening up his playbook.

"I hear you! So, besides whips with secret compartments, what else can I get from the Asian Mafia?" I asked, out of curiosity.

"It's all about establishing a relationship, amigo. I introduce you for the transport vehicles, and where your relationship goes from there is your business," he said bluntly.

"I understand!" I responded.

"But, amigo, I can't introduce you to the Asian Mafia with you dressed like that," he said, gesturing with his finger towards my attire.

"What's wrong with my fit?" I asked defensively, knowing I was fresh to death from head to toe.

"I mean no offense, amigo. But, in the big leagues, jefes don't wear clothes hanging off their asses. We dress as businessmen and wear suits! If you look like a thug, you attract attention of policia. With a suit, you blend in with the elite class, and that's half the battle," he insisted.

"I don't have a suit," I said, wondering what I would even look like in one.

"Don't worry, amigo, tomorrow we get you a suit, and we set up meeting with Asian Mafia."

"Beep … beep … beep …" We were interrupted by what sounded like a garbage truck backing in.

CHAPTER 67

We went out back and I seen a yellow school bus backing in. Not a big yellow bus, but the short style.

"Your new ride, amigo," Pelón revealed.

All I could do was shake my head. *Man, I hope nobody sees me driving this mu'fucka'!* I was thinking, but: "Thank you, amigo," is what I said.

I recognized the driver as one of the Mexicans from yesterday. This time he wasn't pointing a chop at me!

"Paperboy, this is Toro. Toro, this is Paperboy." Pelón introduced us.

"Mucho gusto," Toro said, shaking my hand.

"Mucho gusto," I repeated, assuming that it meant 'nice to meet you.'

"Come look, I'll show you how everything works," Pelón suggested, as he climbed inside the school bus.

He jumped in the driver's seat and I followed him inside. Then, he closed the door behind us: "You have to close the door for it to work," he said, as he started the bus. "Then, you push in the brake and put the gear in neutral," he instructed while doing so. "Then, you put the A.C. all the way on cold and hit the left blinker. In that order," he continued as he followed his own instructions.

I heard a pop and the sound of pressurized air escaping. The sounds came from the stairs on the entrance.

"That's the air-tight seal, so policia dogs can't pick up a scent. Now, you can turn everything off, put it in park, and open the door. Come look," he instructed, stepping off the school bus.

I stepped off, and he reached into the entrance, lifting up the back wall between the last stair and the floor of the bus. Doing so revealed a secret compartment under the entire floor of the bus. It operated on a conveyor-belt type of system. We loaded ten bricks, by pushing in one after the other. Then, Pelón flipped a switch under the floor, moving the bricks out of sight. Once out of sight, he flipped the switch off, and we loaded another ten bricks. We continued the process until all one-hundred bricks were concealed in the hidden compartment. Then Pelón flipped the trap door back down and closed it.

"Now, amigo, you repeat the same combination, but instead of the A.C. and left blinker, you turn on the heater and right blinker. This will seal the compartment air-tight," he explained.

"Sounds easy enough to me," I said, understanding the different combinations.

"Okay, amigo. Now, show me," he challenged to see if I really understood.

I climbed back on the school bus, sat in the driver's seat, and went to work. I recited the steps out loud to myself as I performed them: "Close the door, start the bus, push in the brake, put it in neutral, heater to seal, and the right blinker." I completed the process and heard the sound of the compartment being sealed.

The hundred bricks were sealed air-tight, and I was ready to hit the road!

CHAPTER 68

"Okay, amigo, you're all set. Meet me here mañana, same time, and we'll get you a suit before we go meet with Asian Mafia," Pelón said.

"I'll be here. Just so you know, amigo, I'ma get dropped off in about an hour to get my whip," I informed him, so he understood I'd be bringing someone else to the location.

"Sí, amigo, you have my permission," he said.

"I'll catch you in the morning." I ended our conversation as I jumped in the yellow school bus. Then I called Kendra.

"What's good, Mob?" she asked when she answered.

"Can you meet me at my spot in like, thirty minutes? I'ma need a ride," I asked, hoping she wasn't busy.

"It's all good. But, you better have a blunt ready," she joked, even though I knew she was serious.

$$$$$

I pulled up in front of my spot, and Kendra was already there.

"What the fuck you doing driving a school bus?" she asked, as I climbed out.

"If only you knew! There's some real Mob shit going on right now," I replied, keeping her in suspense.

"Like what?" she said, looking at me like I was trippin', because she couldn't figure out how a school bus could be linked to some Mob shit.

"I ironed shit out wit' Pelón, and a lot of things are going to be changing around here. The Mob just hit the big leagues, baby!" I explained, without saying too much.

"That's what the fuck I'm talkin' 'bout," she beamed, taking in the good news.

"Come help me get this side gate open, so I can park this bus in the back," I said, requesting her assistance.

She followed me to the side of the house where the fence was. It was on a hinge, so you could open it and park a boat or motor home on the side of the house. I'd never opened it before, and it was locked.

"Fuck! I don't have the key to this fuckin' thing," I said in frustration.

"You don't need one; all you need is a hammer," she said with a wink, reminding me how she'd opened Jackpot's "Treasure Chest."

"I have a hammer! Hold on," I said, as I dipped off to get a hammer.

I came back with one, and handed it to Kendra, so she could do her thing. Two good swings was all it took, and the lock was busted open. Then she opened the fence, and I pulled the school bus in, parking it.

"Let's mob," I said, as Kendra was closing the gate.

"Where we going?" she asked.

"To Oakley. I need to grab my whip," I answered.

"Bruh, I still don't understand how that fuckin' school bus has anything to do wit' some Mob shit?" she admitted, obviously puzzled.

"It's not just any school bus. It's a transport vehicle and there's a hundred bricks in a hidden compartment on that bitch!" I finally told her.

"Put that on the Mob," she requested, not believing a word I just said.

"That's on the Mob!" I swore.

"Oh, shit! You're serious!" she said in disbelief.

"Ya' damn right! From now on, y'all gettin' the bricks for twenty bands instead of thirty apiece. Also, it's time to start networking, we're about to start supplying the whole Bay wit' the work!" I explained.

Fa' sho', Mob! We finna take over," she exclaimed.

"You have no idea. This is just the beginning."

CHAPTER 69

The next morning, my alarm clock woke me up from a nightmare, which was a dream that basically replayed the shootout I had with them niggas in the Brownies: "I gotta find out who them nigga are and eliminate 'em!" I said out loud to myself.

It was only five a.m., and I knew Teardrop would be sleeping, but I decided to call him anyway.

"What's up, bruh?" Teardrop asked, sounding half asleep. Probably wondering why I was calling him; it was usually the other way around.

"Bruh, remember them niggas that tagged me?" I asked, knowing he did.

"Yeah?" he answered simply, still half asleep.

"I want them found and eliminated! Ten bricks!" I said, putting a mountain of snow on their heads.

"Consider it done, Mob!" Teardrop responded, sounding fully awake!

Since I didn't know exactly who them niggas were, I had faceless enemies. I'd never been in such a vulnerable position before, where I didn't know who my enemies were. It was as if I was funkin' with ghosts. A known enemy is fair, but one that stays in the dark is deadly. If they seen me, they'd have the upper hand, because I wouldn't even recognize them as a threat. I wasn't feeling the thought of that at all!

$$$$$

It was 7 a.m., and the sun was burning bright. Pelón and I were sitting in our usual spots at the table. He was telling me that we had an appointment with his tailor at noon, and another with the Asian Mafia at two. Since we had some time to kill, Pelón decided to open the playbook in his mind.

"Amigo, it's time for you to establish your organization so you operate it from the background. When it comes to policia, you want to be out of sight and out of mind. They can't stop what they can't see. You never want to be in the spotlight, you have to take over the dark. Staying under the radar and out of the watchful eye of policia is hard! But, it is also possible and absolutely necessary," he said, making his point very clear.

"That does make sense, and I'm only in it for the fortune, not the fame," I agreed, letting him know I was on the same page.

"Bueno, amigo!" he said, pausing for a second: "I know you understand this, so I will move on to my next topic," he continued.

"I'm all ears, amigo," I said, giving him the cue to continue.

"One more thing, very important: you're going to be making mucho, mucho dinero, amigo, so you have to open businesses and learn how to wash your dinero. You start with one 'front' business, and then another, and another. The profit from the first one opens the next one, and so on and so forth. Whatever you want to open, you pick! Just make sure everything appears legit on paper, and you're bueno, amigo," he said, as he continued teaching me the essentials, I needed to learn in order to be prosperous in the big leagues.

"I know what you mean, amigo, and I have some ideas for businesses," I said, as my wheels were turning.

Every time I was locked up, I'd pass my time by reading. I've read a lot of books, but focused mainly on business books. I enjoyed them because I was learning and exercising my mind like a muscle. The way I looked at it, I was already doing time. So, I might as well invest it wisely by learning all I could.

By reading and studying business books, I felt I was investing in my future. It was like a drug; the more I learned, the more I wanted to learn. I had composition books for my notes, and I would read any business book I could get my hands on. I'm glad I did, too, because I was going to flood the whole bay with the finest coke, and use the money to build an empire.

CHAPTER 70

Pelón took me to his tailor, an Italian guy named Gio. Gio did his thing, taking all my measurements, and an hour later he had the crisp black suit I'd picked out ready for me. I tried it on, and even though the tightfitting material felt odd on my body, I looked like I was fresh off Wall Street. My thug-like appearance was completely gone, and the mirror reflected a successful businessman!

"You see, amigo? In this business, as in any business, appearance is important!" Pelón said, smiling and nodding his approval.

I told Gio that I wanted two more, one in gray and one in blue. With matching shoes!" I said, putting in my order.

"Excellent! They'll be ready this time tomorrow," Gio said.

As I was paying the man, he threw in a custom-made shoulder holster. "On the house," he said, with a wink. I did see him glance at my gun when I was undressing for measurements. I threw my previous fit into a bag and walked out wearing the suit with my gun secured unnoticeably under my suit jacket. I was definitely ready for our meeting with the Asian Mafia.

We went to 'Frisco and pulled up to the back gate of some car dealership a little before two. We were on time. Some Asian cat in a dark burgundy suit approached the driver door.

"Can I help you, sir? Customer Service is in the front of the dealership," the man said.

"I am Pelón. I have a two o'clock meeting with Hanh," Pelón informed the man.

"Give me a second, sir," the Asian cat said, disappearing behind the gate.

A few minutes later, the back gate opened and Pelón pulled in. He drove past the garage area where cars were being worked on, and he pulled up to another gate. A few seconds later, that gate opened as well. There was a wide variety of vehicles parked in multiple rows. It was a dealership, in the back of a dealership. Only this one had everything from work vans, SUVs, taxis, limos, and just about any vehicle you may want.

Instantly, a blood red IROC 'Maro with white rally stripes caught my eye: "That mu'fucka' is saucy," I said to Pelón, as I pointed it out to him.

We parked, and another Asian guy approached. He wore a black suit similar to mine.

"Hanh, this is Paperboy, the business associate of mine I was telling you about," Pelón said, introducing me.

"Good to meet you, Paperboy. I'm Hanh," he introduced himself, extending his hand.

"Nice to meet you as well, Hanh," I said, looking him in his eyes as I shook his hand.

"So, Paperboy, I hear you're interested in some transport vehicles?" he said, getting straight to business.

"Yes, I am! Are all of these for sale?" I asked, still eye-balling the IROC.

"Yes, sir. Everything you see has hidden compartments for transport, and is for sale," he said, gesturing towards all the vehicles.

"Okay, good. For now, I'll take a taxi, two white work vans, and that IROC! But I'll definitely be back for more," I said, being decisive.

"That will be two-hundred thousand dollars for all four. The white vans come with company logos of your choice; I'll give you a list to pick from. Also, here is my business card, for future business," he said, obviously liking the way I conducted business.

"Okay, perfect! I'll be here tomorrow morning with the payment and my drivers. Is that okay with you?" I asked Hanh.

"Yes, sir. I'll have the vans ready with the logos, as well. Now, let me show you how to operate the compartments," he agreed. Then he led me to the vans first.

All the vehicles had different compartments. In the floors, trunks, seats, and dashboards. They all opened with similar combinations as the school bus, and were air-tight to conceal the scent from police K-9s in the event of a search.

I ended up picking a plumbing company logo for one van, and a cable company logo for the other.

"What time should I be here?" I asked Hanh.

"We open at 7 a.m." was his answer.
"I'll be here," I informed him.

CHAPTER 71

The next day, me, Jacka, Rydah, and Teardrop all piled into Kendra's whip. We stopped to pick up my suits form Gio, and then we mobbed out to 'Frisco. When we got there, Rydah jumped in the taxi, leaving the work vans to Jacka and Teardrop. They already knew the blood-red IROC was all me!

"Careful in this, my man. That's not a stock engine under the hood. It has every single upgrade possible, and is built strictly for speed!" Hanh informed me.

I started it up, and the Flowmaster exhaust rumbled underneath me. I hit the gas, and a roar escaped as the engine shook from the horsepower: "Hell, yeah! This mu'fucka' is definitely fast!" I said, with excitement.

I pulled out the parking lot sideways, leaving a cloud of smoke for the Mob to follow. And just like that, we were on our way back to the "P" in our new transport vehicles. On deliveries the compartments would hold the work, and on return trips they would hold the money, which is important, because money is well known to be covered in drug residue, and large amounts of money can be easily sniffed out by K-9s. All drivers had to have valid Ls and no warrants.

Everything was coming together better than I could've ever expected.

$$$$$

In the few months I'd been out, I had accomplished more than most people do in a lifetime. I was 21 years old, at the beginning of my reign, and ready to diversify by investing drug profits into multiple businesses. Erasing Jackpot and re-connecting with Pelón had the Mob completely taking over. We had the streets of the Bay on lock!

Word had spread fast, and we were networking with respected bosses from every urban ghetto in the Bay. Opening up our operation to the whole Bay and spreading the wealth, had us making connections that would surely grow over time. What had started as only Vallejo, Richmond, Berkeley, Oakland, Hayward, E.P.A., and 'Frisco, quickly spread outside the Bay to Sacramento, Stockton, and Fresno. The Mob had Cali's coke game sewed up.

Money was coming in fast, so I was investing it right into businesses. I started with a barbershop. I had one Mob member that was skilled with his clippers working it. Then I hired three more barbers that were also well known to be skilled with the tools of their trade. We funneled money through the barbershop by "inflating" the rent we charged monthly per chair, but only on paper! In no time, the barbershop was the hottest one around, and had a legit reputation for the finest cuts!

Then, I went on to start a clothing company that made "I Rep Da Bay" T-shirts. Some of them had all the hottest Bay Area cities printed on them, and others had just the area codes printed on them. We supplied every urban clothing shop in the Bay with these shirts, and they were flying off the racks. The dope money bought the inventory, and we paid our taxes for the sales of the shirts, leaving us clean money to put in the bank.

Next, I used the clean money from the barber shop and the clothing company to open a Roto-Rooter plumbing franchise. It only cost me thirty-five thousand to get started. I already had a work van with the Roto-Rooter logo on it, so it made sense. I contacted Hahn from the Asian Mafia, and grabbed three more vans to go with it. At that time, Hanh opened the door to crates of weapons, fake IDs, and passports.

From there, Pelón gave me some game on flipping cars and houses that are purchased from auctions. So, I opened a used-car dealership, and sold the cars I got "for the low" from auto auctions, "for the high!" I was also hitting foreclosure auctions and flipping houses. I'd use legit money to purchase the house, then use dirty money to fix it up, and quickly sell it for a profit. I took a couple losses, but it was still worth it for the large amounts of clean money received.

Now, I was on the hunt for my castle, and was searching high and low for one that was fit for a king!

CHAPTER 72

One day I was going through the foreclosure listings, and went to check out a few of the houses to see if I'd be interested in flipping them. I was always looking for run-down ones, that needed some fixing up. One house in particular was located in Alamo, California, which is an upper-class area, where houses sell for top dollar. As soon as I pulled up, I knew I'd found my dream house. It was a two-story mini-mansion on five acres of land.

"Oh, yeah! I'm definitely buyin' this mu'fucka'. I don't care how high the bids go, it's mine!" I said out loud to myself after the winding road I was travelin' stopped at a large gate. Behind the gate I could see my future home off in the distance.

The auction was scheduled for the weekend, and it was all I could think about. My spot in Parkside was straight, but it wasn't fit for a Mob Boss! The mini-mansion, on the other hand, absolutely was! Every king must have a castle, and this one revealed the proper level of wealth and power.

$$$$$

"Bids will be starting at ten thousand," the auctioneer announced.

"Ten thousand!" A fancy upper-class-looking white lady yelled out.

"Ten! Do we have twenty thousand?" the auctioneer asked the crowd.

"Twenty!" A Mexican guy who you could tell was a painter by the paint splatter on his pants, yelled his bid.

"Twenty! Do we have thirty thousand?" the auctioneer asked.

"Fifty thousand!" I yelled, jumping in and drawing a little attention from the crowd.

"Fifty! Do we have sixty?" the auctioneer asked.

"One-hundred thousand!" the fancy white lady yelled, jumping the bid.

"One-hundred! Can we get one-hundred and fifty thousand?" the announcer yelled, seeing the obvious interest in the house.

"Make it two-hundred thousand!" I shouted, also jumping the bid, and hoping to quiet the crowed once and for all.

"Two-hundred it is! Do we have two-fifty?" the auctioneer asked, scanning the crowd.

"Two-fifty! the fancy white lady spat, getting frustrated.

It was obvious the bidding war would be coming down to me and her. If I had to bet, I'd put my money on myself for sure!

"Two-fifty!" Do we have three-hundred thousand?" the auctioneer asked.

I was getting frustrated myself, and wanted to shut miss fancy-pants up for good: "Five-hundred!" I barked, jumping the bid again, and hoping that would seal the deal.

"Five-hundred! Do we have seven-fifty?" the auctioneer asked, raising the stakes even higher. "Five-hundred going once … five-hundred going twice …," he continued.

"Seven-fifty!" Miss Fancy-pants smirked, probably just trying to run up the bid, so she could drop it on me.

I wasn't tripping, it's nothing to a boss: "One million!" I barked before the auctioneer could even speak.

"One million! Do we have one-point-five?" the auctioneer asked. "One million going once … one million going twice … Sold! to the man in the gray suit," the auctioneer yelled, declaring me the victor of the mansion.

CHAPTER 73

I pulled up to my new crib, turned off the engine, and sat back taking in the landscape. The spacious six-bedroom, four-bathroom, mini-mansion was the type of house I'd been dreaming of owning ever since my block-ballin' days. I remember pitching nickels and dimes, day and night, goin' hard and showering every couple of days, while sometimes sleeping in bucket-ass cars or abandoned houses. My only goals were to get rich and to buy myself a fat-ass crib.

Now look at me; not only was I making it snow in the Bay, like the winter in Alaska; but I'd just dropped a mill-ticket on a mini-mansion – one that is complete with a resort style swimming pool, a basketball court, a two-bedroom guest house, and a separated five-car garage, all of which are sitting on five acres of land, providing plenty of privacy from neighbors.

"The big leagues! This is what it's all about!" I said to myself, as I fired up a blunt. As I admired my new crib, I seen a deer with two babies trotting across my property.

All I had to do now was get my secret room built, get a security system installed, and have a fence put up around the property, one that would keep the deer out and my pits in! They were getting an upgrade theirselves, from the small back yard at the Parkside house, to several acres they could roam free on.

I had two monstrous pits. My red-nose was a female named "Hitter"; the other pit was Kaydah's blue-nose, a male named "Muscle."

When I was grabbing everything outta Kaydah's spot that night, I heard Muscle bark and decided to grab him as well. I'd been taking care of him ever since. Hitter and Muscle were like brother and sister, which was surprising. Hitter was a full-fledged fighting dog, and viewed every pit as an enemy to kill. But for whatever reason, Hitter wasn't aggressive towards Muscle. She was fixed, as well, so it wasn't like they could mate and make puppies.

When I'd first gotten Hitter, I was only thirteen years old. There was a litter of pit bull puppies, and I had the pick of the litter. So, of course, I started picking each one up by the loose skin and fur on the back of the neck, and then I'd shake it! If it cried, I tossed it back and tried another one.

When I was done, there was only two puppies that didn't cry, and one even growled at me. So, I took both of them and started bumping their faces together. Doing so caused the one that growled at me to snap at the other one. The other one just accepted it, so it was obvious who the "pick of the litter" was. Based on her aggressive nature, I named her "Hitter"; it turned out to be perfect.

When I was fourteen years old, and Hitter was about a year, I fought her for the first time. I was walking her and letting her run wild in one of the city park's baseball diamonds, when three niggas a few years older than me approached. They came up on the other side of the fence with a pit of their own; a coke-white red-nose. The instant Hitter seen the other pit, she was trying to attack it through the fence.

Their pit was just sitting there; it wasn't barking, growling, or anything else, and they were asking, did I want to fight my pit with theirs? The way Hitter was trying to get through that fence, I knew she was ready! Their soft-ass pit wasn't ready for nothing. The way I seen it, Hitter wanted to fight, so I let her!

CHAPTER 74

Them niggas let their pit loose in the dugout, where the baseball players would sit during games. Once their pit was in, I pulled Hitter up. It was as if she knew what time it was already. She got quiet and her hair was standing up all the way down her back. I held her by the collar and took her leash off. Then, I opened the dugout gate.

She was in there in a flash, on full attack mode, and they were fighting. Then, like a trained killer or a pit that's been in many battles, she went in for the kill. She lunged in and snatched their pit by the throat. As soon as Hitter bit down, she locked on! Then, she started shaking like crazy. She'd shake for a few seconds and then pause, shake again for a few seconds and pause. Hitter repeated this shake and pause method, until all she had between her locked jaws was a victim.

Hitter won her first battle, and we both seemed to be hooked! I realized I had a real hitter on my hands, and she was living up to her name. With each and every kill after that, Hitter and I both were falling in love with the sport. It even seemed to make our bond a little stronger. One of the crackheads that frequented my block said it was because I was allowing her to do what she was made to do: Fight!

It turned out that the crackhead used to fight pits back in his day. He also knew I had a real hitter on my hands, and said it often. Before I knew it, he was giving me all the game he had on fighting pits. For one, he told me to never clip Hitter's ears, like so many who fight pits do, because the ears give the other dog something else to lock on.

"While the other pit is locked on her ear, Hitter can get inside to the throat!" the crackhead explained, making perfect sense.

He also taught me about starving her for a couple days before a fight. He said the hunger triggers the killer instinct. Then he had me get Hitter a harness with a long chain, and connect it to a tire. By her pulling the tire behind her while she ran, she filled out her loose skin and bulked up. Her strong muscular build and wider neck complemented her already big head, and made her look like a monster!

Muscle wasn't a fighter like Hitter, but he wasn't soft, either. Muscle was vicious as fuck and was more of a people eater. He did not like humans. Kaydah and myself seemed to be Muscle's only exceptions.

"He knows not to bite the hand that feeds him!" Kaydah used to say.

Kaydah was serious, and wouldn't let anyone but me feed Muscle.

CHAPTER 75

Over the last year, I'd made many moves that shaped my immediate future and ultimate destiny. My boss status was well respected, and the Mob itself was expanding throughout the whole Bay. We were recruiting bosses from every major city; we united the ghettos of the Bay by operating as one Mob! The organization I'd formed had turned a dog-eat-dog world into a family of bosses that ate together. So, I decided to do it big and throw a Mob celebration at the mini-mansion for my 22nd birthday. One that would represent the Mob's success and welcome our new brothers to the family.

$$$$$

I had my eye on a possible protégé that I could bring up and mold, like Kaydah did me. It was my young nigga Husalah. He was only sixteen years old, but his potential was evident. The young nigga started out with a zip and bubbled it to a brick with a quickness. Needless to say, the name Husalah definitely suited bruh. He even had his own trap, and that mu'fucka' was generating traffic.

Husalah was mixed, and his light skin had him look more like a pretty boy than a gangsta'. But his looks were deceiving. Even though he focused more on the money aspect of the game, he surely wasn't to be underestimated. He was a born hustla' for sure, and getting money came natural, but he was also known for lettin' that choppa' spray.

Hus' was ready for another brick, but little did he know: I was going to drop an extra three bricks on him! I grabbed the bricks, tucked them in the IROC's stash spot and headed to his trap.

When I got there, Hus' and a couple other young niggas were sitting around playing Nintendo. Hus' looked up as I walked in, and I motioned for him to come holla' at me in the kitchen.

"What's up, Mob?" Hus' greeted, as I gave him dap.

"Shit, I got this work for you. You got that money?" I said, getting straight to business.

"Yeah, let me grab that for you," he said, as he slid out the kitchen and down the hallway.

He returned, handing me four different stacks of money wrapped in rubber bands, which I knew was obviously five bands in each stack, since he was paying twenty Gs for the brick. I put the money in my pockets without even counting it.

"Looks like business has been good lately! I pointed out.

"Real talk, shit's been boomin'," he agreed.

"I've been peepin' how fast you're coming to re-up, and I believe it's time for me to give you a lil' more weight to push around," I said, tossing Hus' the duffel with the work in it.

He caught the duffel, unzipped it and looked inside. A smile instantly spread across his face as he realized it was four birds instead of the usual one.

"You shouldn't have a problem movin' that, right?" I asked, already knowing the answer.

"Hell, naw, Mob! They don't call me Husalah for nothing," he responded.

"I already know! When you have the other sixty bands, hit my line, and I'll drop another four bricks on you. Once that's gone, you should have enough to pay me and grab four more! You feel me?" I asked.

"On the Mob! I'll be ready," he agreed.

"Fa' sho'! Peep game though, my nigga; instead of sitting up in this mu'fuckin' trap, playing Nintendo all day, you should be killin' time by reading!" I stated, ready to give bruh some game.

"Reading?" he responded, like I was speaking a different language.

"Not just reading, but studying! I'm talkin' 'bout business, my nigga. You need to be learning what them white folks never wanted us to learn. Business is the secret to gettin' out the game!" I explained, dropping a jewel.

"Get out the game? What if I don't want to get out the game?" he asked, still naïve to the realities of what comes with the game.

"You see, the game usually leads to one of two outcomes – prison or death! It's a vicious cycle that keeps cops, D.A.s, and judges employed. They all have a piece of the drug pie, either directly or indirectly. Cops are either paid under the table or promoted to detectives or captain after a big bust.

D.A.s get convictions and become senators or presidents. One hustla' off the streets and in prison could launch and elevate the careers of four white men. That's why they don't want us to learn how to do it right." I paused to let my words sink in. "The purpose of getting in the game, is to get rich and get out! The problem is, we get addicted to the money and the lifestyle that the game brings. We're never satisfied. The money we take risks to make, we should be investing in legit business. But instead, we throw it down the drain just to take more risks. In the game, the more risks you take, the better the odds are of you getting caught or getting shot," I continued explaining, to make my point.

"I'd never looked at it like that," Hus' admitted.

"Exactly! Not many do, and that's what them white folks want. By learning business and investing your dope money, you are still getting paid! But you're getting paid in a way that doesn't lead to prison or a grave. You're basically hustling smarter, not harder," I said, educating Hus' and opening his mind to a different way of thinking.

"That's some real-ass game right there, Mob! I'ma definitely start reading business books," he stated, understanding the bigger picture.

"Don't just read – study! Take notes and everything! Then take what you learn and put it into action," I encouraged.

"I got you!" he said, soaking up game.

"So, can yo' niggas hold down the trap while you mob with me for the night?" I asked Hus'.

"Fa' sho'! Where we going?" he asked.

"To a party!"

CHAPTER 76

The party was poppin'. It was a perfect eighty-five degrees outside, and we had the barbecue blazing. The smell of baby-back ribs and hot wings filled the air. We had an open bar with bottles of whatever you wanted to sip on. There was also plenty of weed, and coke to go around for those who indulged.

The women were beautiful, and of every nationality. They all knew there was plenty of competition around. So naturally, they got creative as they tried to stand out and catch the attention of the bosses in attendance. My backyard looked like the Playboy Mansion. The resort-style swimming pool was mostly occupied by women in thong bathing suits with their ass-cheeks hanging out. A handful of them even decided to go topless!

It was as if the pool was made for topless women, considering it never got deeper than three feet. I was enjoying the sight of all the topless women, when one of the baddies caught my eye. Most of her body was tatted up, and it definitely enhanced her sex appeal. I found her intriguing, and her beautiful eyes demanded my attention. We frequently locked eyes, but I was waiting for the right time to make my move. Like a real Mac, I wanted to flirt with some of the other women, and make her jealous first.

While the women in the pool were going topless, there were others dancing and shaking their asses to the Too-$hort we had knockin'. There was also those women who chose to present theirselves as more "lady-like." It didn't matter what role they chose to play, they all had one thing in common; they were blatantly seeking attention from the bosses.

The bosses were stuntin' their asses off, fitted up from their hats to their shoes, and rockin' all of their jewels, of course. They had their eyes on the women and were ready to run their A-game. Because there ain't no mobbin' without mackin'. Anybody who was anybody in the Mob was present, and Hus' knew his presence signaled a major leap in status; he officially had boss status! He'd been moving a lot of weight, and that means money. Which in the Mob, never goes unnoticed.

I let the crowd know that the guest house was open for anyone who wanted to get their freak on. I already knew the Mob would get it poppin', so I put a bowl full of condoms in the living room and in the kitchen. Then, I decided to go chill in the pool with a pretty-eyed baddie who was waiting for me. I peeled out of my shirt and pants, revealing my muscular frame and tattoos. The women were hootin' and whistling as I dove in with nothing but my boxers on. I couldn't help but laugh as I dove in and swam up to miss pretty-eyes to conversate.

She was a pale-skinned Latin Princess that was rocking blonde hair. She introduced herself as Blanca, and seemed delighted by my open admiration of her sexiness. I bit my bottom lip while I took in her nudity up close.

"It's a pleasure to meet you, Blanca. I'm Paperboy," I said, introducing myself with a smile full of girls' best friends.

"Oh, no, honey, the pleasure is all mine," she replied with a smile of her own.

"So, what's good, sexy? You interested in taking this party up to the V.I.P. section?" I asked, referring to my master suite and not wasting any time.

"Wow! You don't waste any time, do you?" she asked with a giggle.

"I sure don't! Do you?" I asked, as I bit my lower lip again.

She laughed before she spoke: "I'm down, as long as my friend is invited!" she declared, putting her arm around the topless model-looking woman next to her.

I looked at her friend, and she licked her lips seductively, letting me know she was down as well.

"It's all good! She's invited, too!" I responded, trying to hide my excitement.

As we climbed out of the pool, my eyes went on a trip. They started at Blanca's pretty eyes, then went down to her exposed breasts, before traveling further south to her fat, jiggly ass that had a light case of cellulite. She was short, only about 5'4", and thick in all the right places. Then they shifted to her friend, who was taller with an athletic frame. Her titties were small but perky, and she had a small, firm ass to match. She wasn't my type body-wise, but the beauty and sexiness of her face made up for it!

I could tell they were an experienced tag-team duo, and knew they planned on blowing my mind!

CHAPTER 77

I was sitting in my room, in the center of my couch, with my pants down around my ankles. One woman was on each side of me, and they both were leaned into my lap, giving me fellatio as they tag-teamed my pole. My head was thrown back, and my eyes were closed, as the sounds of slurping echoed through the room. One of them began sucking on my balls, while the other focused on the head of my shaft with tongue and lips.

I stood tall and firm as they serviced me. Before I knew it, I was feeling the tenderness of a nut building up. I clenched my ass-cheeks and stiffened my legs as I fought back the explosion that ensued.

"Oh, shit," I whispered as one of them took me deep into her throat. As she was slowly throating my every inch, I felt myself beginning to climax. My body tensed up as I pulled my tool out of her mouth and started stroking it. Both women extended their tongues and connected them side by side at the tip of my cock, giving me a place to unload.

The sight alone sent me over the edge. As I exploded my load, they licked up everything that came out! Then, they began French-kissing each other, as I sat there enjoying the show. The experience had me in sexual overdrive, and I was still hard as a rock. So, I got up and pulled both women over to my king-sized bed.

I put a magnum rubber on and bent Blanca over doggy-style. I couldn't wait to get inside her guts. The thinner one's name was Amber, and she jumped on the bed and scooted up to Blanca's face with her legs wide open. Blanca instantly put her tongue to work on that pussy. While I was beatin' the pussy up, I had my eyes on Amber, as she was rubbing her nipples and biting her bottom lip. She was surely enjoying Blanca's head game. The show was intoxicating, and it had my dick so hard, it probably grew two more inches.

Blanca's pussy was extremely wet, causing me to slide completely out of it a few times while I thrashed it. I watched Amber reach a climax as she threw her head back moaning loudly. I decided to switch so she could return the favor to Blanca, while I beat up her guts for a while. I slid inside Amber and was amazed by how tight her insides were. I looked down and watched my pole disappear and reappear as I pounded Amber's guts full-throttle.

Within minutes, I had Amber moaning as she tried her best to focus on pleasing Blanca, who was also moaning herself. I was already starting to sweat and wasn't even close to my second nut. I was ready to switch again, but this time I wanted Amber to ride me while Blanca sat on my face, and I put my tongue to work. It was definitely going to be a wild and erotic night.

$$$$$

It was almost midnight, and a car was sitting in the drive-through at a Jack In the Box. The occupants were half-drunk and waiting to order when a black Suburban pulled up unnoticed. Two men bounced out in all black, with ski-masks pulled down over their faces. The bogeymen. They were both armed with AK-47s as they ran up on the side of the car in the drive-through. They were sitting ducks, blocked in with cars in front and behind them. They didn't even have a chance to reach for their guns, before flashes of fire kissed the night, as the shooters unloaded their extended clips. The car rattled and shook from all the rounds ripping through the metal.

$$$$$

The sound of my phone ringing woke me up from a deep sleep. It was early in the morning, and I was in bed with two naked bitches. Memories of our sexual escapade came flashing back to me.

"Yeah?" I answered, hung over and still half-asleep.

"Turn on the Fox news!" Teardrop requested.

I did, and seen a black car sitting in a Jack In the Box drive-through with so many holes in it, it looked more like a cheese grater. The news reporter was informing the public that there were no survivors and no suspects.

237

"Okay! What am I watching here?" I asked.

"Eliminated," Teardrop said simply, informing me that the job was done, and I owed him ten bricks.

CHAPTER 78

The Mob's lucrative coke operation had skyrocketed over the past year. So much so, I had to start grabbing between two-hundred and three-hundred bricks at a time just to keep up with demand. I was now supplying every major city in northern Cali, and that meant delivering anywhere between twenty and sixty bricks a drop, depending on the city.

Oakland led all cities, averaging sixty bricks a drop. Next came 'Frisco and Sacramento, averaging about fifty bricks a drop. Stockton and Fresno averaged about forty bricks, while smaller cities like Pittsburgh, Vallejo, and E.P.A., averaged about twenty bricks a drop.

I was ready for another three-hundred bricks, so I was having a meeting with Pelón. While doing so, he came at me with a new proposition. I had been lining up all of my ducks, because I was getting ready to open a tow truck company. Pelón liked the idea and was proposing that I use the tow truck company to transport my own work from down south.

Pelón explained that he had to focus more on other states in order to expand his operation. So he proposed that if I transported my own work from LA back to the Bay, I'd get the bricks at a discounted price of eight Gs a kilo. That meant a $600,000 discount on three-hundred kilos. How could I refuse?

It was Pelón's job to get the work into the U.S. The only thing separating Mexico from the massive American market is the border. While it's true that the countries share a two-thousand-mile land border, and all of those miles can be and have been used to smuggle drugs, it's also true that some of those miles are infinitely more valuable than others. The vast majority of the border runs along isolated desert, but the valuable real estate is the "choke point" cities of Tijuana, Ciudad Juarez, Nueva Laredo, and Matamoros. And the reason lies not in Mexico, but in the United States. It has to do with highways. Tijuana borders San Diego, where Interstate 5 is the major north-south artery that runs to Los Angeles. From Los Angeles, product can be stored and moved up the West Coast, or anywhere in the United States.

The action is in using trucks for transportation. Because the 1994 NAFTA treaty between the United States and Mexico had recently passed, thousands of trucks were crossing the border from Tijuana every day. Most of them carried legitimate cargo, but many of them carried drugs. And given the sheer volume of traffic, U.S. Customs couldn't come close to searching every truck. Even a serious effort to do so would cripple U.S.-Mexican trade. Not for nothing was NAFTA often referred to as the "North American Free Drug Trade Agreement." Once the truck with the drugs in it crosses the border, it's literally on the freeway, which made Interstate 5 one of the arterial veins of the Mexican drug trade.

Once the cocaine was safely in the U.S., Pelón would have cars or trucks packed with bricks. And by packed with bricks, I mean hidden in the door panels, in the gas tank, under the seat, behind the lining of the trunk, and even in the tires. A Mob member would drive a flatbed tow truck down south to LA, and pick the car up right off the street. To the ordinary eye, it looked as if a broken-down car was being towed away. Then, the car would be brought back to the Bay. And by transporting my own product from LA back to the Bay, I was getting it for a price I was more than happy with.

Pelón was shipping two tons a month into the U.S., most of it over the Tijuana border. But only a portion of it came to the Bay. The rest of it was transported to other states all across the U.S. Money was no problem for Pelón; it was flowing in – cocaine north and cash south.

What the U.S. will never understand or even acknowledge – the so-called Mexican drug problem isn't the Mexican drug problem. It's the American drug problem. There is no seller without a buyer. As long as there is an appetite for drugs on this side of the border, someone like Pelón will be smuggling cocaine across the border. And someone like me will be selling it.

CHAPTER 79

1996 …

By the time I was 23, I was far more advanced than the average 23-year-old. By getting in the game so young, I'd been schooled by older bosses like Kaydah and Pelón for years. This allowed me to learn from their mistakes and successes, so every move I made was sophisticated and kept me advancing in the game. You have to be well rounded; one-dimensional people go nowhere in life. So if you want to move up in the game, you'll first need to spread out. And not only did I have tremendous hustle and street smarts, I knew how to use the power of a bullet – all of which served me well in the Mob.

The realization that I was willing to do whatever was necessary to reach my ends, opened my eyes. I've been obsessed with guns and the lifestyle of a drug dealer for as far back as I can remember. Not having a positive influence in my household led me to the streets, where I ultimately became fully committed to the game. It wasn't long after that that I was drafted into the Mob.

My whole life I've been a student of the game. Like a sponge, I always soaked up everything I could. But there's always a point when the student becomes the teacher. And as the leader of the Mob, I had many valuable lessons to teach the organization. But out of all the important lessons I've learned over the years, a few stand out the most. 1) Never fuck with niggas that are hindered by their own stupidity, or fall victim to their emotions – like love. 2) The streets are a war zone, and any type of fear for blood or death will bring you defeat. 3) The game is about learning, applying, advancing, stacking, and investing. 4) Out of all the different enemies I'd encountered, the pigs are the worst.

Now, at 23 years old, I was still linked in with Pelón, getting kicks of coke, dirt cheap, and making a killing in the streets. I only sold to D-Boys, and I never sold nothing under a brick. I had a strong team of go-getters from all over Northern Cali, who were flippin' shit quick, and bringing in fast money.

So fast, it was time to make another power move, and I had the perfect plan. …

CHAPTER 80

Even though I'd never been a rapper, I've always been around the rap game, so I understood the ins and outs when it came to utilizing rap music for business purposes. By that, I mean starting a record label and using it not only to make money, but to wash money.

From everything I'd learned over the years, I knew the key to my success would be to play the background and avoid the spotlight at all costs. So, after getting everything up and running, my role would be to run the operation from behind the scenes.

So that was the plan: to start a record label and have a rap group. I wanted at least four or five rappers in the group. Reason being, with more artists, we could wash more money, and keep everything looking legit. We'd do so by releasing group albums, solo albums of each artist, and collaborative albums with other hot artists. The more albums we released, the more money we could wash!

Finding rappers was the easy part; I had them right in the Mob. I'm talking real street nigga's that had gas, but never pursued music, because they were too caught up in the streets. However, I knew once I painted a picture, like Picasso, they would jump on board.

I called up three of my Mob niggas from the Lo: Rydah, Jacka, and Husalah; and two other Bay niggas, FedEx and AP .9. I called them to the roundtable for a meeting. Then, before they arrived, I put all the money I needed, "washed," on the table, for motivational purposes. When they stepped in, all eyes were glued to the money, and it provided a sort of adrenaline rush for everyone. We were all paper-chasers, and at that moment, I knew they would get with the program. The look in their eyes told it all; they knew the meeting was going to change their lives.

"I called y'all here for this meeting, because I'm ready to make a power move. One that I believe will take the Mob to the next level. But, it requires a certain skill set and passion that you five possess." I paused for effect, and they all looked around at each other, obviously wondering what I was getting at, "I'm going to introduce you all to a whole new way of life. I have a master plan, and all the resources to make it a reality. But, I can't do it without y'all. I'm talking about a plan that will bring all of us a lot of money. More money than y'all will know what to do with!" I paused again, letting the anticipation build. "I'm presenting an opportunity to put you all in a position of power, wealth, and fame! My plan is to start a record label and rap group, so that we can utilize the rap game to expand our drug operations nationwide," I informed them, finally getting to the point.

No one spoke. But, as the idea sunk in, smiles spread across their faces. They'd all been rapping for years, and were finally being presented with an opportunity to turn their passion for rapping into a career.

"We're going to use the music to wash money and eventually expand our drug enterprise, by pushing product state to state. We already have Cali on lock, so now is the time to work towards taking over the nation. But, the rap game is just like the dope game; you have to blow up in your home region, first, then expand! Y'all will be the rappers, and my role will be to play the background, keeping everything running smooth and looking legit. That way we can keep our operation off the feds' radar," I explained.

I finished laying out my plan, purpose, and mission. Then, I painted the visual for the short- and long-term goals. By the end of the meeting, they fully understood. We weren't just building a rap group, but an organized crime operation that would extend far and wide.

It was during that meeting that the Mob Figgaz was born. After everything was agreed upon, I got up and snapped a picture of them gutta-ass niggas fresh out the street, sitting around all that money. It was to serve as a reminder of where we came from and where we were going. That picture is what ultimately became the Mob Figgaz' logo that you still see today.

In the Mob, everybody has a position, role, and purpose, all of which are beneficial to the objectives of the Mob. The Mob Figgaz were the face of the operation. They attracted the spotlight that came with the fame and fortune. Behind the scenes, however, I was the mastermind that ran the operation – as a ghost; doing so was a must, because I knew the feds would come snoopin' around, trying to associate the label with crime. So going undetected while making the label appear clean was my number one priority. With that goal in mind, I made it clear that they were not allowed to speak my name in any of their songs. But, they could reference me in ways that nobody would know who they were talking about. I also refused to appear in any photos, because everyone knows the feds love using photos to build cases.

CHAPTER 81

While the Mob Figgaz worked relentlessly on writing hits, I was working on a production and release plan. I had many connections in the rap game, so I decided to explore my options. In the end, I worked a deal with Sacramento rapper C-Bo. For a brick, he agreed to record, "present," and help promote our first album. By using 'Bo, it gave us an immediate buzz, because we were associated with a factor in the West Coast rap game.

After I dropped 'Bo off his brick, my IROC broke down. One of 'Bo's homies had a 1972 Cutlass for sale, so I bought it on the spot! It didn't have a tuck spot, so I had to be careful as I headed back to the P. I crossed the Antioch bridge and hit Highway 4 on my way to run another play. I was riding dirtier than a bum's fit, so you know I was doing the speed limit. I had my Mack 11 with the 30 clip, two bricks of yola, and about 20 bands.

Next thing I knew, I was getting lit up by Highway Patrol. Ain't' this a bitch!? I would've tried to see if maybe I could just get a ticket and go, but with my record and no Ls, it was too risky. That meant I fa' sho' had to take him on a high-speed to try and shake his bitch-ass.

I decided to pull over. This would give me a head start, because I would wait until he walked up to the side of the car to smash off. I figured by the time he got back to his car, I'd already be in and out of traffic. The Cutlass was fast; it definitely had a monster under the hood.

I pulled over and cut the engine off so the pig wouldn't get suspicious, but I kept my fingers on the key so all I had to do was start up and go. The pig got out, walked behind my shit, then up the passenger side. As soon as he got by the door, I fired up the engine and gassed off. Doing so must've startled the pig, because when I looked in my rear-view, I seen his bitch-ass scrambling off the ground and running to his car. In a matter of seconds, I was hittin' 110 easy, in and out of lanes. I could still see the pig, but he was way behind me, so I tossed the Mack and started plotting my next move.

CHAPTER 82

One thing I learned about high-speeds is, if you're gonna get away, you gotta do it quick. Otherwise, before you know it, there will be ten more pigs and a ghetto bird involved. So that was the idea. To get away quick!

I hit the Harbor Road exit in the P and made a left. As soon as I got to Railroad, there was a PPD black-and-white sitting at the light. There must've been an alert out on my car already, because he hit his lights instantly. Plan "A" was a no-go, but I had everything in a Gucci duffel sitting in the back seat, so Plan "B" was to shake the pigs and toss it.

My nigga Bone stayed in Parkside, so I hit the nigga with my TracFone, and told him to post up by the tracks. The new plan was for me to shake the pigs long enough to smash by and toss the bag so Bone could grab it and go. I told him if it worked out, he'd get a brick, and he was with it.

Screams of sirens filled the air as cop after cop joined in on the chase. I was flashing through the streets skillfully maneuvering the whip around turns, getting sideways and shit, while showing my handles off to the onlookers that had begun to gather. I was trying to stay in the area so I could toss the duffel. I smashed down Warren Way and bent a right on N. Parkside Drive.

Halfway through the turn I must've hit the gas a little too hard, because the whip lost traction and I slid right into the ditch next to the tracks. This was the first time I'd ever bapped a whip (and the last, for the record), and before I could even attempt to bounce out and run, the pigs were already on me with their guns drawn.

"Fuck!" I yelled.

There was nothing I could do. They had me.

I got out the whip with my hands up, laid on my stomach, and crossed my feet. Then I had hella knees and elbows jammed in my back while cuffs were slapped on my wrists. As it turned out, the Highway Patrol lit me up for my tinted windows. Ain't that some shit!?

$$$$$

As soon as my attorney stepped into the room, he loosened his tie and sat down. I'd hired him specifically because he was a beast at getting good deals. His job obviously wasn't to get me acquitted or anything, because I'd gotten caught with the dope and money red-handed. Since that wasn't even an option, his job was to get me the shortest sentence possible. Which is less about his skills as a lawyer and more about his skills as a negotiator. But, his expertise came at a hefty price of 80 Gs.

"The prosecutor really has a hard-on for you, my man. It seems he's going to do everything he can to send you away for as long as possible," he advised, getting straight to business.

"Well, that's why you get paid the big bucks. Do what you can to get me the best deal possible. I know I made my bed, so I'm prepared to lie in it. Just work your magic," I responded.

After months of negotiating and postponing court dates, he brought me a deal for 84 months and said it was the best he could do. It technically wasn't a "good deal," but the prosecutor wasn't doing much budging and would've preferred to send me away for at least a decade. So, I accepted it!

The deal was done and my destiny was to spend the next 84 months (7 years) in a federal prison. It wasn't nothing to brag about, but that's the risks that we take trying to beat the odds. From what I'd always heard, even though you had to bring all your time in the feds, the quality of time was much better than state time.

Well, I'd soon find out.

CHAPTER 83

I was 23 years old and on my way to Lompoc, which is a well-known federal prison in California. When I got there, I walked through the cellblock with my bedroll in my hands. As I made my way to my cell, the sounds of inmates echoed through the corridor. I walked at a slow pace, with my head high. Once at my cell, I seen it was empty and was relieved because I knew I'd be able to pull in a cellie of my choice.

After I put my things away, I made my way to the dayroom. As soon as I stepped in, niggas began to ask me where I was from, so I let it be known I was from the Bay Area.

"Yeah, I figured you was," said one nigga, "you got some folks right over there." He pointed to a group. I pushed over and introduced myself as Paperboy, from the Bay.

"What part?" asked a tall, skinny nigga.

"Pittsburg," I told him.

He extended his hand as he spoke: "That's what's up. I'm Dre, from Vallejo."

I knew exactly who he was. Dre was a well-known rapper from the Bay who got cracked with some of his team for conspiracy to rob banks. He even recorded an album over the phone while fighting his case in the Fresno County jail.

Dre and I chopped it up, and realized we knew a few of the same folks. We'd just never crossed paths until then.

"You know how to play chess?" Dre asked me.

"Naw, bruh, I've never played," I lied.

"Well, I guess I'ma have to teach you a thing or two!" he joked, as he pulled out a chess board.

We began to set up the pieces, and he peeped that I knew exactly where to put each piece. That alerted him that I actually did know how to play. A smirk crossed both our faces, and a subtle calm took over as we were ready to have a friendly war. Dre took off his sweater and set it to the side. Then, he moved his first piece, a pawn, and the game began.

It was an intense match to the end, but Dre ended up winning. We ran it back, and the next game resulted in a stalemate. The third match, I won!

Once I got settled in, I got in contact with 'Bo and the Mob Figgaz to link them and get the album in motion. C-Bo told me he wasn't going to drop the album until he knew it was a masterpiece and worthy of his co-sign. I told him I wouldn't expect anything less. I remained in contact with 'Bo and the Figgaz throughout the whole process. I also plugged the Figgaz in with Pelón and kept them grinding.

Meanwhile, Dre and I really clicked on some Mob shit, and ended up celling up together. We both had that "real recognize real" vibe, and within a matter of months, we became brothers behind them walls. Before I knew it, we were bouncing ideas off one another, coming up with plans, plots, schemes, and everything else. Bruh, like me, was money-motivated, so I knew he was someone I could really fuck with on a Mob hype.

I had connections in every aspect of the game, from dope to rap. Dre had a gift, and his rap career was already in motion. In fact, he'd recently released The Rompilation," right from prison. I saw this as a rare business opportunity, and began running Dre down on the operation I'd started with the Figgaz. I wanted to see if he was on the same page, and maybe interested in jumping on board. Not only was he on the same page, he was definitely on board!

CHAPTER 84

The plan was for us to start a new rap label, together, and instead of using it to expand the existing operation, this label would be the 2.0 version, and it would go even deeper than the Mob Figgaz operation. See, the fundamental part of the record label with the Mob Figgaz was basically to wash money. But, since Dre and I had so much time to plot and iron out our plan, this new label would not only be used to wash drug money, but to also promote the product we were making money from. While Dre handled the music side of it, I would take care of the drug portion of the operation.

I explained to Dre I wanted to use the music to promote the drug Ecstasy. Around this time, "E", or "X", was becoming the new "in" drug, and was hitting the Cali scene slowly but surely.

I felt like if we got ahead of the curve on this, we could dominate the market. I explained to Dre that I had a major plug with the Asian Mafia on all the ingredients, pill presses, etc. Dre asked me if I'd ever fucked with it, and what it was like? I told him it was a party drug, and it went crazy!

I couldn't believe Dre had never fucked with E before, but then he reminded me, he'd been in prison the last several years.

"Don't even trip. I'ma go to visit tomorrow, and I'll have my bitch bring us some in next week," I told him. He said he was with it, so I put it in motion, and the next weekend my bitch brought us twenty pills. We ended up poppin', and Dre fell in love! The nigga was "on", rappin' and giggin'! We had our own little party that night.

We continued ironing out the plan, and I let bruh know that the first thing I needed him to do was start the label as soon as he got out. He asked what we were going to call it, but I wasn't sure, so we decided we'd think on it. Then I explained that I needed him to have the label up and poppin' before I got out, so I could do my part right out the gates. He said he would. I also let him know I'd get him some E to flip, as well as give him some dough to get on his feet and start the new label. I was in mid-thought when …

"Damn, Paperboy, my brain is sizzled!" said Dre.

At that point, we'd been poppin' for a couple days straight. That's when a lightbulb went off in the Mac's head: "I got it!"

"Got what?" I asked.

"The name fo' the mu'fuckin' label, nigga!" Dre replied, sounding excited as hell.

"Well, let me hear it then!" I told him.

He gave me a big-ass smile and said: "We gon' call it Thizz. Thizz Entertainment."

He then continued by saying that we'd call the pills "Thizzles."

"Huh?" I said, as I looked at him like he was crazy. "Bruh, we gon' have to cut you off the pills."

Then he ran me down on his train of thought. He explained how after you popped, you couldn't think because your brain is sizzled, and that "Think" plus "Sizzle" is "Thizzle."

I immediately understood, because the shit does sizzle your brain. The thought of it reminded me of that commercial where they show an egg and say, "This is your brain." Then they'd show some eggs frying in a pan and say, "This is your brain on drugs" It all made perfect sense. And that's how Thizz Entertainment was born, and how E became known as Thizzles.

Once we had the name locked in, we continued to focus on the details of the plan. This was crucial, because Dre only had a few months left on his bid. I wanted to make sure all the pieces were in place, and our plan was fail-proof.

CHAPTER 85

1997 …

A couple weeks before Dre was to parole, he came up and told me that he kept catching some nigga mugging him. This tends to happen a lot when word's out that someone will be going home soon. Bitter niggas wanna test them, thinking they won't do anything, for fear of fucking off their release date. Anyway, Dre wasn't feeling it one bit, and said he was gonna dog-walk the nigga if he caught him doing it again. When he said that, I thought, *Fuck that, we need you out there!*

"Look, my nigga," I told Dre, "if he keeps it up, I'll scrape him."

Dre wasn't really tryna hear it, but I had finally convinced him it was in our best interest. We couldn't let nothing fuck off our plans!

The next morning, we were at our table, choppin' game, when Dre said the nigga had walked by, on the track, lightweight mugging again. I could tell he was hot, so I told him if the nigga was still doing it the next lap, I'd give him the attitude adjustment he was looking for.

The sucka came around again and, sure enough, he was mugging. I bounced up and pushed up on the nigga: "What's hatnin'? You got a problem?" Before he could even answer I rocked his shit with a solid right hook. His knees buckled a bit, but he stayed standing and swung. I side-stepped his jab, and rocked him again, this time with a left hook that landed squarely on his "button", causing him to hit the pavement. He tried to get back up, but his legs were rubber and he fell again.

I looked around to see if the guards were on us, and they weren't. I told the nigga if I caught him mugging again, I wasn't going to stop!

"You trippin'. I don't even know what you talkin' 'bout," he mumbled, as he looked up at me cross-eyed.

By this time, niggas began to gather around as if it might crack off, and that caught the guard's attention, so I walked off.

Before I even looked his way, I heard Dre laughing hella hard. All I could do was shake my head as I reached out to shake Dre's hand. He finally stopped laughing long enough to say, "you crumbled that nigga's shit," then he went right back to laughing.

Some of the folks had asked what that was all about, so I filled them in real quick and everything was good.

Two weeks later, after doing a solid year together, Dre was released back to the streets. The last thing he said before he walked out the cell was:

"I know you believe in me, and I won't let you down, my nigga."

CHAPTER 86

Dre got out and went straight to the lab. He recorded what became "Stupid Doo Doo Dumb," which he wrote most of while we were cellies before he got out. In 1998, he moved to Sac, officially started our Thizz label, and dropped "Stupid Doo Doo Dumb" as our first release under the new label.

A year after "Stupid Doo Doo Dumb," and two years into my bid, the "C-Bo's Mob Figgaz" album finally dropped. It was a bit of a challenge to get five street niggas together and focused enough to complete the album, especially with me being in prison, but we got it done.

Both albums were instant hits, and both labels were up and running. At that point, our target markets were the Bay, Sac, and everything in between. We hit the streets with a splash and created major waves in the West Coast rap game; not an easy thing to do, considering they were both new, independent labels. But the initial buzz created an immediate demand for more music, which gave us the momentum we needed to execute our primary mission.

The long-term objective was to build a lucrative drug operation that expanded across the entire nation. In order to do so successfully, we needcd to wash the large amounts of dirty money we'd have coming in. The Mob Figgaz would clean the coke money, and Thizz would clean the X money, but both labels were at the starting point – a foundation to build from. Until we grew, we had the other "front" businesses in place to wash the money coming in.

As the Mob, we'd eventually form alliances with other rappers and street hustla's across the country. We'd establish ourselves as the connect on coke, ecstasy, and of course, that good Cali-bud; these were basically the resources to take our alliances to the next level. We'd use the music portion of the alliances to collaborate, network, and create new business opportunities, using the rappers as "influencers" in their region. This would allow us to sell more music and more product throughout the ghettos of America. And, most importantly, by networking with other rappers across the country, traveling, etc., it would give us an "alibi" – a reason for all the traveling – when the feds came around asking questions. Therefore, every time we traveled somewhere to make a drop, we'd also record a song or two with the local rappers, that we'd immediately release on our next album. Remember: it wasn't if the feds came, it was when the feds came. It was just a matter of time, and we needed to be prepared ahead of time, ya dig?

However, growing the drug operation to this level would have to wait until I got out, since it was my role in the Mob. Meanwhile, the rest of the team needed to focus on making bangers for the streets and building our influence in the rap game. And if it was easy to do, everyone would be factors and superstars; so, I needed them focused!

CHAPTER 87

2003 …

I knocked down my fed time and was back to the streets. It was time to get back to what I'd started, and elevate my plan to the next level. I'd initially started the plan on the streets, but my time in the feds allowed me to link with Dre and transform it to something more elaborate. And now that I was out, I was more than ready to execute the expansion I had in store.

I was fresh out, and anyone who's been locked up knows the first twenty-four hours are always the loveliest. The air smelled fresh, not stale like the recycled air inside prison. The sun shined brighter and seemed to embrace you with a welcoming warmth. Even the mundane sounds of car horns and the hustle and bustle of everyday life was music to the ears of a person who hadn't heard anything for years but the slamming of steel doors and the gravelly shuffle of feet on concrete.

Dre and the Figgaz had done exceptionally well, exceeding all expectations. In 2002, Dre dropped

"Thizzle Washington," and just this year he dropped "Al Boo Boo." Also this year the Mob Figgaz dropped the "Mob Figgaz" album. All albums were hits and both labels were on fire!

It was all perfect timing, too. Since the music side of the operation was poppin', I could slide right in and grow the drug portion of it. It was time to expand.

With the Mob Figgaz and coke, we were ready to start moving kicks state to state; we had the right contacts, and the market was there with a high demand. But with the Thizz and the X operation, we'd have to start from the bottom.

It was a trip how everywhere I went, I heard our music blaring out of cars. If it wasn't Mob Figgaz, it was Mac Dre; and if it wasn't Mac Dre, it was Mob Figgaz. I wasn't hearing anything else! It didn't matter where I was: in traffic, at a stop light, at the liquor store, you name it! And all this motivated me more. I may have been the Mob Boss, but everyone under the Mob was a boss in their own right. And as rappers with a spotlight from the streets, they weren't only bosses, they were also ghetto celebrities.

I had to utilize my Mob ties to the Asian Mafia in San Francisco to get the ball rolling on our X operation. Through them I was able to get everything I needed – pill press; someone to design our different "stamps," which were pictures that we stamped into the various colors of pills, which we also used as a way to brand; and a direct source of MDMA, which of course is the main ingredient.

By the time the lab was up and running, the demand for Thizzles was dramatically increasing. Before I knew it, we were selling out faster than you could imagine. So, I had to revamp the operation by opening up another lab. This one was twice the size of the first, and we were still selling out!

Not that I'm complaining, trust me, it's a great problem to have. Shit, we were selling thousands of "boats" (1000 pills) a week, all over northern Cali – the bay, Stockton, Sac, and even Fresno. At first, depending on the quantity of boats purchased, we were charging anywhere between two and five stacks per boat.

At that time, Thizz pills were going for ten, fifteen, and even twenty dollars apiece, depending on where you were at or who you were getting them from. Every club, rave, and house party was flooded with Thizzles. If it wasn't, the function wasn't poppin'. Straight up. And whoever had the Thizzles at these functions, literally had lines of folks wanting them. With Mac Dre's influence, Thizzin' was the thing to do.

CHAPTER 88

2004 …

While in the feds, I established Mob ties with niggas from all over the U.S. The Ohio niggas, in fact, were waiting on me. They had dope rappers and a huge demand for the bricks, which was exactly what I was looking for in order to expand. So, I got out and started putting plays in motion. And here I was, pressing play on another one: the Figgaz would be transporting fifty bricks to Ohio; recording a couple hits with a rapper that went by Ampichino; and then they'd be on their way back to Cali.

I also decided to throw in a boat of Thizzles on the strength, so they could essentially create a market and a demand for the "newest" and "hottest" drug on the scene – Thizzles! Before I knew it, the Ohio niggas weren't only purchasing bricks, they were also purchasing boats of X.

This strategy worked so well, I decided to do the same thing with the Missouri niggas and Kansas City rapper Fat Tone. So, when he received his bricks, he also got a free boat. I looked at it as a way of promoting the business, and as expected, the Thizzles created an immediate market and demand.

Next thing I knew, I was receiving major orders from both Ohio and Missouri niggas. I decided to send the Figgaz back to Ohio for that drop, and Dre would handle the drop in Kansas City. Reason being: The Jacka was collaborating on an album called "Devil's Rejects" with Ampichino, and Dre was scheduled to perform at a show that Fat Tone had coming up. So both parties had legit reasons to be outta state.

Now that the Thizzle operation was literally poppin', I decided to do a walkthrough and check out the new lab. When I walked in, it was business as usual. Mob niggas were standing guard with AK-47s and naked women were pressing pills with nothing but a face-mask on. I couldn't help but smile, knowing my vision was now a reality and both operations were running smooth. As I walked through the lab, I did so with a ski-mask on to secure my identity.

You never can be too careful.

CHAPTER 89

After I left the lab, I decided to meet up with Abby. After we had reconnected at the strip club, we continued a "friends with benefits" type of relationship. But after I went to the feds, she started writing me and coming to visit, and we decided to make our relationship official again.

After I got out, I had so much on my mind and my plate, I hadn't seen her. I know she assumed I just used her and was ghosting her, but that wasn't even the case. I did feel bad for not contacting her, but I had a major role in the Mob's operation that I needed to fulfill, and I didn't want to get sidetracked. Now that I'd done my part, it was time for me to make it up to her.

When I called, she seemed extremely excited to hear from me, and said it was okay for me to slide through. When I got there, I just walked right in: "Abby," I called out, as I sat down on the couch, feeling a little nervous and excited at the same time.

"Hey, Papi," she said, as she walked into the living room. She was wearing small booty-shorts that barely covered her cheeks. The bottom of her enormous ass was still hanging out and I was enjoying the sight as she walked past me into the kitchen.

She knew what she was doing as she strutted past, working her hips from side to side. Her caramel complexion and dark silky hair made her look like a Latin goddess. She was a stallion. Her thighs were thick and her waist was trim, giving her a perfect hourglass shape.

She returned from the kitchen with a bottle of Henny and two glasses filled with ice. My eyes were glued as she bent over in front of me to place the bottle and glasses on the table. Her fat pussy lips were visible from the back. She had it waxed, nice and smooth, how I liked it. Out of habit, I smacked her ass. On cue, she began to wobble it just as my hand lifted off her plump cheek.

She turned around and slowly straddled me, putting her weight on me. I instinctively placed both of my hands on her ass and gripped her cheeks. She licked her full, slightly oversized lips, and started slowly grinding her pelvic area into my lap. I smiled as her magic was working, causing my manhood to lift up and poke her.

She smiled back and was grinding right on it! I knew she was getting moist between her legs when she moaned softly and started rubbing her nipples though her shirt. Her tits were big, round, and soft. She didn't have on a bra, so her erect nipples were bulging through her T-shirt. They stuck out like two bullets. I was done with the foreplay; it was time to get busy!

CHAPTER 90

I stood up, stripped completely naked, and then sat back down. She quickly climbed back on top and started kissing me, as she reached down and swiftly slid my thick cock inside herself. Her booty shorts were moved to the side, giving me easy admission to her warmth. She was soaking wet in anticipation; she bit my lower lip as I slid deep inside her.

Her coochie was tight, and extremely wet, causing wet noises to fill the air as she bounced up and down. I was rock hard and had reached my full potential. She threw her head back in pure pleasure as she smacked down on my lap, taking me all in. I gently bit on her left nipple through the T-shirt, and was gripping on her booty as it pounded thunderously with each landing.

All of a sudden, she jumped off me and dropped her booty shorts to the floor. She then turned around and sat back down on me in the reverse cowgirl position. She placed her hands on the coffee table and began twerking on my pole.

I watched in amazement as she made me disappear and reappear repeatedly with each twerk. I was fresh out, and hadn't built my stamina up yet. So,

I was close to releasing, but I wasn't done just yet. So I stopped her, slid out, and pushed her off me. Then I stood up and tossed her onto the couch. I grabbed both of her legs and gently pushed them back to the point that both of her feet were behind hcr head. I glanced down and her juicy lips were glazed as her erect clitoris was exposed.

I slid back inside her and began to grind in slow, circular motions. She was moaning loudly as I maneuvered my tip to hit all of her walls. Baby was an all-out freak, and our sexual chemistry was strong. It didn't take me long to hit the point of no return, so I pulled out and started stroking myself.

Without hesitation, Abby sat up and began giving me sloppy fellatio. I ejaculated and she moaned as she caught everything I let out. I grabbed the back of her head and my legs got weak as she sucked and swallowed until there was nothing left.

I knew she didn't get hers, so I was determined to run it back and beat it up until she screamed for mercy. But first, I needed a break and a few shots of that Henny.

$$$$$

It was about 3 a.m., and I was dead asleep, when my phone began ringing non-stop. Abby was cuddled up on top of me on the couch, and I had to get her off me so I could reach my pants and grab my phone: "Yeah, what's up?"

"Bruh, Dre is dead."

CHAPTER 91

𝕿𝖍𝖊 𝖁𝖆𝖑𝖑𝖊𝖏𝖔 𝕿𝖎𝖒𝖊𝖘
Bay Area Rapper Mac Dre, Dead

A San Francisco Bay area underground rap star, who police say was also a member of a gang of robbers, was killed in Kansas City, Missouri, when a gunman shot into a van in which he was riding.

Andre Hicks, 34, known as Mac Dre, was killed about 3:30 a.m. Monday, when another vehicle pulled up beside the driver's side of the van he was in and began shooting, police said.

The van swerved across the highway median, across the southbound lanes, and down a steep embankment. Hicks was thrown from the van, but police said he died from the shooting. The driver crawled from the wreckage and walked for help.

Hicks had performed at a concert in Kansas City on Friday night, and stayed in the area during the weekend.

Police were trying to deter-mine a motive, Captain Vince Cannon said. Witnesses did not hear Hicks arguing with anyone, and officers do not believe the shooting stemmed from road rage, Canon said.

Hicks has recorded more than a dozen albums since 1989. In the early 1990s, police began invest-igating Hicks and several as-sociates thought to be members of the Vallejo, California, Romper Room Gang, which was suspected in a string of bank and business robberies.

Hicks was eventually charged in federal court with conspiracy to commit bank robbery, after he and several others were arrested while preparing to rob a bank. "We were on his tail for a long time," Vallejo Police Lieutenant Rick Nichelman said.

Hicks recorded raps mocking law enforcement, often naming specific officers, including Nichel-man, who was a lead investigator in the case.

Nichelman said some of the lyrics were reportedly recorded over the phone while Hicks was in jail awaiting sentencing. Hicks was released from prison in 1997.

CHAPTER 92

Just thinking about the death of Dre brought back so many memories from the past. Especially the good old days, when we first met in the feds. Back when we built our bond behind them walls, and first started forming the plan that became the foundation of the Thizz empire. Some of y'all might be wondering how I could look back on my days of incarceration and consider them the 'good' days. I'll admit, it does sound crazy. But, crazy or not, I found myself wishing I could have those days back. At least then, the Mac was alive.

I remember when I first got out and Dre threw a huge party for me. It seems like it was just yesterday. He wanted to make sure it was poppin' in a real way, so everybody who was somebody in the Mob was there. As I surveyed the room, I quickly realized that a whole new generation of bosses had popped up during the time I was gone. Of course, many names reached me while I was locked up, but I was finally able to put faces to names and meet my new brothers.

Dre was really feelin' himself that night. He had the whole spot live, like a concert. I can still picture him giggin' and shit with his signature 'Thizz face' on. Just thinking about it now makes me grin. Dre's wild-ass was Thizzed out of his mind! We had so much fun, it was more like a frat party than a Mob celebration. But that was Dre; he definitely knew how to live life …

My bad; I got lost in my thoughts, reminiscing. Back to the story; them Kansas City niggas stole our brother's soul, and they gotta pay for that!

CHAPTER 93

Immediately after Dre's death, I held a Mob meeting and needless to say, it was an awkward one! The occupants of the room included Mob members from all over the Bay, all of whom were top bosses in their respective areas.

Everyone in the room was completely silent, and we all seemed to be staring at Dre's empty seat. Noticing the uneasiness, I stood up and walked behind Dre's chair; I felt goose-bumps travel up my arms as if I was feeling Dre's presence.

"We have suffered a great loss, but business must go on. Dre wouldn't want it any other way. I'm not saying it won't be a struggle, but the struggle runs through our blood. It's in our bones, in the water we drink and the air we breathe. We didn't choose this life; we were born into it. We literally come from struggle, so we know how to use it as motivation. Which helps us flourish and overcome unfavorable odds. Most, if not all of us, come from roach-infested homes, which are broken because our mothers are on dope and our father are either in a cage or a grave. So, growing up, all we had was the streets. All we had was the Mob, and together, as one Mob, we rose above the struggle and now run these streets!"

The men around the room nodded in agreement.

"As for the KC niggas; they're gonna get exactly what they got coming. And when we clap back, we're going to send a message that clearly expresses the wrath of the Mob!" I said, slamming my fist on the glossed-oak table. "But we won't allow our pain and anger to cause us to move sloppy. Every move we make will be calculated as usual. We're going to find out who was involved, and every single chess piece connected to Dre's death will be wiped off the board," I continued, as I returned to my seat at the head of the table.

Rubbing my hands together, I sat there in deep contemplation, exercising my strategic mind. At times like these, I was a genius at playing mental chess with the opposition. We had a feeling Fat Tone was behind the hit, especially since nothing happened in Kansas City without Tone at least knowing about it.

I was in mid-thought, when my phone started ringing. Normally, I wouldn't answer my phone in the middle of a Mob meeting; but I had been waiting on this particular call: "Yeah?"

I remained silent while the person on the other end gave me the information I was looking for. Then, without saying another word, I hung up.

CHAPTER 94

"Our source has come through for us; Fat Tone was indeed involved in Dre's death, but he wasn't the trigger man. Turns out, Tone sent his right-hand man, Cowboy, to do his dirty work. In any case, they both are going to pay, and now that we have the answer we were looking for, it's time to start strategizing our plan to clap back," I explained to the Mob, trying my best to contain my anger and the beast within that was more than ready to surface.

When you're ranked as a Mob boss, you don't have to put in the work, from a drug transaction to a Mob hit! But that wasn't how I operated! I chose to lead by example and show the Mob that we truly are brothers. That no one man's life was worth more or less than another's. This was important to me, because a true leader only becomes one by the quality of his actions and the integrity of his intent. So, off top, when the opportunity presented itself to body them niggas for killing our brother, I fo' sho' had to be the one pulling the trigger! There wasn't a question or second thought about it. That's just how it had to go down.

We knew with everything going on with Dre's death, bringing it to them in Kansas City wouldn't be smart. The pigs were everywhere, investigating, and Fat Tone and his crew knew we were trippin'. So, he likely had his goons ready, locked and loaded, and on high alert for any outsiders. Especially Bay Area niggas, and we fo' sho' stand out.

We also knew Tone wasn't stupid enough to come to Cali. Shit, the whole Bay Area wanted Fat Tone's head, so we would have to figure something else out.

Tone started reaching out to the Mob, denying any involvement and assuring us that whoever was responsible would pay. We did not feel the need to give him a heads up that we'd already confirmed exactly who it was, and that, yes, they would most certainly pay. Instead, the Mob chose to let Fat Tone think we believed him. We even told him the driver of Dre's van confirmed that the shooting stemmed from road rage.

Nevertheless, we knew Tone wasn't stupid enough to completely let his guard down, so we decided to slow-play the situation and work on gaining Tone's trust little by little. We started by letting Tone know we wanted to continue with the drug operation, but with all the heat surrounding Dre's death, we'd have to let shit die down first.

CHAPTER 95

Damn. I'm really about to bury my nigga, I thought in disbelief as I looked at myself in the mirror. I took a deep breath as I looked into my own eyes. They were red and full of sadness. My designer suit was tailored to my muscular frame, and my broad shoulders held the material nicely. A long Cuban-link gold chain hung around my neck, displaying the Thizz Nation logo with Dre himself in the middle.

The limo pulled up and blew its horn. I quickly reached under my bed and snatched the duffel bag that contained bricks of pure white cocaine. I figured I might as well drop off some product to the fellas, since we were all headed to Fairfield for Dre's wake anyway.

The limo ride was silent, as I tried to wrap my mind around the death of my brother. I had a deep nagging pain in my heart, and the stress of retaliation on my brain. *I can't believe he's gone*, I thought, while I dreaded laying my nigga to rest. I needed to calm my nerves, so I fired up a blunt of some Grand-

Daddy-Purple. As soon as the smoke hit my lungs, I felt a calm sweep over my body.

When we pulled up to the church, the nervous energy returned. I had to prepare myself for what I was about to do; it was time to say goodbye to a loved one. The wake was held at Fairfield's Mount Calvary Baptist Church, and it seated about 2000 people. That obviously wasn't going to be enough. It looked like the President of the United States had died, and it was his viewing, rather than that of a local rapper. It was obvious that Mac Dre was street royalty, and a well-respected Bay Area legend. The whole Bay-Area community seemed to've showed up in full force. It was a sad day in the Bay!

The Mob walked up and surrounded the vehicle as I stepped out. We all walked into the church together, and I shook my head as I saw the casket that held my brother's soulless body.

I headed towards it.

When I finally reached the casket, I was overcome with anger at the sight of Dre's lifeless body laying before me. The gloss that his dark skin had once possessed was gone, and his eyes had sunk in. I took off the Thizz chain and set it on his chest: "I'ma get them niggas," I quietly pledged to my brother. Then I turned with the poise of a Mob boss and took my seat.

Dre's funeral was held the very next day at Oakland's Mountain View Cemetery. The service was to be officiated by a former Oakland Raiders football player, Pastor Jerone Davison of Fairfield's Bountiful Harvest Ministry Church.

282

The funeral was chaotic. So much so, the Mob had to assume the role of sentries and guard the entrance. We tried to get a list written with Dre's mother Wanda so we knew who to let in; but that almost seemed to make things worse, because not all the loved ones made it on the list. There were just too many names for Wanda to remember and write down, especially under stress of having to bury her baby. So, we ultimately had to have family members start "clearing" loved ones to enter.

We had to do it that way because in some cases, guests were included on the list, but not their children or spouses. In other cases, people not on the list were allowed in before others who were. At one point, we were calling out names, and they were relayed through the crowd. The person whose name was called then pushed his or her way through to the chapel doors and was let in, with the door immediately closing behind them! If you weren't cleared to enter, you definitely weren't getting past the Mob.

CHAPTER 96

2005 …

By mid-February, three months after Dre's death, the dust seemed to have settled, so we decided it was time to put things in motion. We contacted Fat Tone and let him know we were ready to re-open the operation.

As always, we liked to make things look music-related, and since Mac Dre was gone, we decided to link Tone up with Mac Minister. Mac Minister was a "promoter" we had stationed in Las Vegas, where he also operated several of the Mob's "escort" services. Nothing sells better than sex, and no city in the world sells more sex than Vegas. Mac Minister was already pimpin', so when it was time to open the escort services, I felt Minister would be best to run it. The escort services provided it all; in calls, out calls, a dating service, topless or nude cleaning services, and massages that came with "happy endings," three-somes, dominatrix, and, of course, women of every shape, size, and color. You name it!

We needed to make sure Tone lowered his guard, so Minister's primary objective was to gain his trust, by any means necessary. I knew Minister was game-tight. My only concern was that he tended to be hot-headed and impulsive, so I stressed to him the importance of remaining calm, cool, and collected. He assured me there was no need to worry.

To test where Fat Tone's head was, regarding trust, we set up the initial meeting in the following month, in Vegas. We wanted to see if he'd leave Kansas City and come out West.

He did. And the initial meeting between Mac Minister and Fat Tone went even better than expected. Mac showed Fat Tone the Vegas high life – drugs, gambling, money, and hoes. He took him to all the hot spots, gave him a tour of the escort services, then plugged him with the product he actually came for; so he could get his traps "boomin' " again in Kansas City. In his eyes, everything was back to normal.

Since that went well, the next step was to assist Tone with his career in the rap game. Tone desperately wanted to be a 'real' rapper, and the Mob's connections in the rap game extended far and wide. After pulling some strings, Mac Minister took Tone out to New York to meet some 'mainstream' rappers. "This nigga wants to be a rap star so bad, and I got him thinkin' he gon' be the next 'Pac!" Mac Minister said during a phone call we had while he was in New York.

Once Mac Minister expressed that he'd fully gained Fat Tone's trust, I decided it was time to call a Mob meeting so we could figure out the details. I set it up for that Easter weekend.

$$$$$

The Mob was gathered at the roundtable, ready to strategize the most critical part of our mission: the hit!

CHAPTER 97

Everyone knows the key to developing a successful plan starts with figuring out the five Ws: Who, What, When, Where, and Why.

The 'Who' seemed to be the hardest of them all to figure out. Niggas practically started fighting over who would have the honors of bodying Fat Tone. There wasn't a soul in the room that wasn't ready and willing. The job was like a fish in the middle of a bunch of hungry sharks. Little did they know; my mind was already made up! It would definitely be me that revenged Dre's death and bodied Fat Tone.

I also needed Mac Minister (obviously, because he was the one who had gained Tone's trust), and I decided to bring along a prospect who'd been getting pulled into the Mob by Mac Dre himself. I needed a get-away driver, and the young thug had a reputation as a highspeed specialist.

The 'What' was basically a no-brainer. We would just line up another 'transaction' with Fat Tone to lure him to a spot where we could execute the hit.

The 'When' came surprisingly easy. In fact, it seemed like Minister had thought of it ahead of time. "Snoop Dogg has a concert in Vegas coming up soon. I can tell Fat Tone I got him plugged in to open for Snoop," he said.

"How soon?" I asked.

"Towards the end of next month. The 24th, I believe," Minister answered.

"That'll work," I said. "He already knows we like to keep everything music-related, so we'll set up his next 'pick-up' at that time. Purchasing product and opening for Snoop Dogg will get him there and have him ego drunk. We'll get it done during that time, maybe a couple days before the show."

We all agreed.

And last, but definitely not least, the 'Why' was already written in blood.

The meeting with the Mob went well, and because we chose to keep our enemy close, the foundation for our plan was easily formed.

Check!

CHAPTER 98

On May 20th, a little over six months after Dre was shot and killed, it was time to make our move. Minister called Tone with the good news: in addition to Fat Tone coming to Vegas for the transaction, he would also be opening for Snoop Dogg. Tone was beyond excited.

$$$$$

On the 22nd, while Tone was on a red-eye to Las Vegas, I made a detour and stopped by Dre's grave, before also heading to Vegas. It had been months, and this was the first time I'd been back to visit Dre's resting place. It was time to visit my bro and blow a blunt with him. I got out the car and walked up to his headstone. A spectrum of emotions shot through my body: "That nigga is about to get what he's got coming, real soon, my nigga!" I said, as I fired up the blunt. "I'ma send him your way, so you can handle him again when he gets there!" I continued, and the thought of that brought a smile to my face.

As I smoked the blunt, I knew things would never be the same without Dre. Not only because he was so instrumental in the Mob's organization, but because I'd lost my brother. Unfortunately, that was all a part of the game. Because of the bay-area lifestyle the Mob led, the possibility of death or a cage was always high. The same way we would down a nigga with no hesitation, the streets were full of mu'fucka's who would do the same. I just never thought it would happen to the Mac.

I hit the blunt one last time and closed my eyes. I could picture my nigga's face, and I felt a closeness as if he was standing right there next to me.

I jumped back in the whip and went to meet up with the prospect, so we could make our way to Vegas.

$$$$$

The prospect, his ho' bitch, and myself pulled up to Minister's. We slid up in the ho' bitch's whip, since it was legit, yet also couldn't be traced back to the Mob.

While we waited for Tone, we discussed specifics. Then, as is customary in Vegas, the prospect put his ho' bitch to work. She was left in the dark on the whole situation, and was only there to do what she did best.

Around the time Fat Tone was scheduled to arrive, Minister went to the airport to pick him up. When he got there, he was met with a surprise. Tone wasn't alone: he brought his own ho' bitch, as well as his right-hand man, Cowboy. *Perfect*, Minister thought to himself. *The Mob gods* are setting things up perfectly.

As they drove to Minister's spot, Minister ran down the specifics of the plan, the parts that Fat Tone was supposed to believe:

"I got a legit whip in my bitch's name that we use for trips. It has a secret compartment. Not only are you welcome to use it while you're out here, you can use it to transport the work back to K.C. – unless you'd rather slide in a rental," Minister told him.

Then Minister continued: "The transaction is scheduled to go down tomorrow night at 11:30. This time we'll handle business at the housing development down the street. I don't do nothin' here no mo'. My spot's been hot, wit' all these nosey-ass neighbors," he said, as he nodded towards a neighbor they saw lookin' in their direction.

Tone agreed, and thanked Minister for everything. Afterwards, he mentioned he was getting a room at the MGM, and planned on dropping his ho' bitch off on the blade and hitting the town for some gambling, which he loved to do. Minister threw Tone the keys to the under- bucket. "Do what you do. I'll meet you at the MGM tomorrow night, and we'll meet up wit' the connect from there," Minister said.

CHAPTER 99

Around 10:30 the following night, Minister pulled up to the MGM. He met up with Tone and Cowboy, then they headed to the parking garage to retrieve the under-bucket. All three loaded in, then made their way to the meet-up spot.

Once there, they found themselves waiting … and waiting. Minister was getting frustrated and angry with me. I should have been there already!

"I'ma call this nigga and see where the fuck he at," Minister said, as he stepped out the car for some privacy. While he was talking to me, I informed him that I was just around the corner. He looked into the car window and saw Tone get on his phone. After Minister hung up, he got back in the car, just as Tone was ending his conversation with, "I'ma call you as soon as I get back to the hotel."

"This nigga right around the corner," Mac Minister said. A couple minutes later, they saw headlights. Minister told Tone, "Flash your headlights, so he can see where we at."

The prospect drove up, flipped a bitch, then he backed up to Tone's car so the trunks were a few feet apart from each other for an easy swap.

"Pop the trunk," Minister said. "I'll make the swap." Then he got out the car and met me between the two bumpers. He grabbed the money out of Tone's trunk, and I told him to wait right there until I started bustin', and then to jump in the car with the prospect. Fat Tone looked in his rearview, but couldn't see much, because his trunk was up. When he looked in his side-view mirror, he saw me coming from behind his car and up the driver's side with a duffel bag.

The gravel crunched under my feet as I slid up the side of the whip. And like an animal hunting its prey, my killer instincts kicked in. Even with the element of surprise, there could still be a fire fight.

I could imagine Fat Tone thinking, "This nigga finna show me the work."

But, Tone would have been wrong. Very wrong. When I reached into the bag, I came out with an AK-47 with an extended clip. Before Tone's brain could even register what was happening, he saw it pointed at his face. Then I let it bust and bullets tore through the windshield and into Tone's face and chest. Cowboy jumped out of the car and started running. I seen him reaching for his waist, so I quickly sent some rounds his way, hitting him in his back. Tat! Tat! Tat! Tat! He screamed as he fell.

I hit Tone a few more times, even though it was clear he was already dead. Chunks went missing from Tone's face as he lay slumped over. Then, I went to finish off Cowboy, who was in a puddle of his own blood, trying to crawl away. Cowboy turned on his back and began begging for his life, as I approached with the K pointed at him. Once close enough, I peeped a gun lying next to Cowboy – he'd dropped it when I tagged him.

"Y'all thought you could body a nigga from the Mob and get away wit' it? This is for Mac Dre, you bitch-ass nigga!" I sprayed bullets across Cowboy's legs. We don't call AK-47s chops for nothing; the K bullets damn near chopped his legs off!

"Aaaaahhhh! Please, don't kill me," Cowboy cried. Him begging for his life was music to my ears: "Checkmate! You're already dead, bitch-ass nigga," I replied. Then I smiled as I emptied out the rest of the clip into the nigga. Tat! Tat! Tat! Tat! Tat!

In the Mob, money and murder went hand in hand. So, killing them niggas was nothing because it was survival of the fittest. I went about killing just as a surgeon would go about performing a surgery: with expertise and precision.

"Let's go, nigga!" the prospect yelled out to me from the driver's seat of the car.

I picked up Cowboy's gun off the ground, then jumped in the car, and we sped off.

When we got a safe distance from the murder scene, Minister opened the bag of money. It was filled with stacks of hundred-dollar bills. However, under a few layers of bills, it had cut-up newspaper rubber-banded into the stacks. *What the fuck?* Minister thought to himself. Then it hit him.

"Paperboy, them niggas was gonna burn us!" Minister said.

"What you mean, 'burn us,' nigga?" I asked, confused.

Minister flipped through one of the stacks, revealing the layers of paper cut the same size as money.

Then I thought about the Glock I'd picked up, and I understood exactly.

We went and scooped up the ho' bitch from the blade, and headed back to the Bay, slapping Mac Dre the whole way.

To be continued...

THE CELL BLOCK

BOOK SUMMARIES

MIKE ENEMIGO is the new prison/street art sensation who has written and published several books. He is inspired by emotion; hope; pain; dreams and nightmares. He physically lives somewhere in a California prison cell where he works relentlessly creating his next piece. His mind and soul are elsewhere; seeing, studying, learning, and drawing inspiration to tear down suppressive walls and inspire the culture by pushing artistic boundaries.

THE CELL BLOCK is an independent multimedia company with the objective of accurately conveying the prison/street experience with the credibility and honesty that only one who has lived it can deliver, through literature and other arts, and to entertain and enlighten while doing so. Everything published by The Cell Block has been created by a prisoner, while in a prison cell.

THE BEST RESOURCE DIRECTORY FOR PRISONERS, $17.95 & $5.00 S/H: This book has over 1,450 resources for prisoners! Includes: Pen-Pal Companies! Non-Nude Photo Sellers! Free Books and Other Publications! Legal Assistance! Prisoner Advocates! Prisoner Assistants! Correspondence

Education! Money-Making Opportunities! Resources for Prison Writers, Poets, Artists! And much, much more! Anything you can think of doing from your prison cell, this book contains the resources to do it!

A GUIDE TO RELAPSE PREVENTION FOR PRISONERS, $15.00 & $5.00 S/H: This book provides the information and guidance that can make a real difference in the preparation of a comprehensive relapse prevention plan. Discover how to meet the parole board's expectation using these proven and practical principles. Included is a blank template and sample relapse prevention plan to assist in your preparation.

THEE ENEMY OF THE STATE (SPECIAL EDITION), $9.99 & $4.00 S/H: Experience the inspirational journey of a kid who was introduced to the art of rapping in 1993, struggled between his dream of becoming a professional rapper and the reality of the streets, and was finally offered a recording deal in 1999, only to be arrested minutes later and eventually sentenced to life in prison for murder... However, despite his harsh reality, he dedicated himself to hip-hop once again, and with resilience and determination, he sets out to prove he may just be one of the dopest rhyme writers/spitters ever .... At this point, it becomes deeper than rap .... Welcome to a preview of the greatest story you never heard.

LOST ANGELS: $15.00 & $5.00: David Rodrigo was a child who belonged to no world; rejected for his mixed heritage by most of his family and raised by an outcast uncle in the mean streets of East L.A. Chance cast him into a far darker and more devious pit of intrigue that stretched from the barest gutters to the halls of power in the great city. Now, to survive the clash of lethal forces arrayed about him, and to protect those he loves, he has only two allies; his quick wits, and the flashing blade that earned young David the street name, Viper.

LOYALTY AND BETRAYAL DELUXE EDITION, $19.99 & $7.00 S/H: Chunky was an associate of and soldier for the notorious Mexican Mafia – La Eme. That is, of course, until he was betrayed by those, he was most loyal to. Then he vowed to become their worst enemy. And though they've attempted to kill him numerous times, he still to this day is running around making a mockery of their organization .... This is the story of how it all began.

MONEY IZ THE MOTIVE: SPECIAL 2-IN-1 EDITION, $19.99 & $7.00 S/H: Like most kids growing up in the hood, Kano has a dream of going from rags to riches. But when his plan to get fast money by robbing the local "mom and pop" shop goes wrong, he quickly finds himself sentenced to serious prison time. Follow Kano as he is schooled to the ways of the game by some of the most respected OGs whoever did it; then is set free and given the resources to put his schooling into action and build the ultimate hood empire...

DEVILS & DEMONS: PART 1, $15.00 & $5.00 S/H: When Talton leaves the West Coast to set up shop in Florida he meets the female version of himself: A drug dealing murderess with psychological issues. A whirlwind of sex, money and murder inevitably ensues and Talton finds himself on the run from the law with nowhere to turn to. When his team from home finds out he's in trouble, they get on a plane heading south...

DEVILS & DEMONS: PART 2, $15.00 & $5.00 S/H: The Game is bitter-sweet for Talton, aka Gangsta. The same West Coast Clique who came to his aid ended up putting bullets into the chest of the woman he had fallen in love with. After leaving his ride or die in a puddle of her own blood, Talton finds himself on a flight back to Oak Park, the neighborhood where it all started...

DEVILS & DEMONS: PART 3, $15.00 & $5.00 S/H: Talton is on the road to retribution for the murder of the love of his life. Dante and his crew of killers are on a path of no return. This urban classic is based on real-life West Coast underworld politics. See what happens when a group of YG's find themselves in the midst of real underworld demons...

DEVILS & DEMONS: PART 4, $15.00 & $5.00 S/H: After waking up from a coma, Alize has locked herself away from the rest of the world. When her sister Brittany and their friend finally take her on a girl's night out, she meets Luck – a drug dealing womanizer.

FREAKY TALES, $15.00 & $5.00 S/H: *Freaky Tales* is the first book in a brand-new erotic series. King Guru, author of the *Devils & Demons* books, has put together a collection of sexy short stories and memoirs. In true TCB fashion, all of the erotic tales included in this book have been loosely based on true accounts told to, or experienced by the author.

THE ART & POWER OF LETTER WRITING FOR PRISONERS: DELUXE EDITION $19.99 & $7.00 S/H: When locked inside a prison cell, being able to write well is the most powerful skill you can have! Learn how to increase your power by writing high-quality personal and formal letters! Includes letter templates, pen-pal website strategies, punctuation guide and more!

THE PRISON MANUAL: $24.99 & $7.00 S/H: *The Prison Manual* is your all-in-one book on how to not only survive the rough terrain of the American prison system, but use it to your advantage so you can THRIVE from it! How to Use Your Prison Time to YOUR Advantage; How to Write Letters that Will Give You Maximum Effectiveness; Workout and Physical Health Secrets that Will Keep You as FIT as Possible; The Psychological impact of incarceration and How to Maintain Your MAXIMUM Level of Mental Health; Prison Art Techniques; Fulfilling Food Recipes; Parole Preparation Strategies and much, MUCH more!

GET OUT, STAY OUT!, $16.95 & $5.00 S/H: This book should be in the hands of everyone in a prison cell. It reveals a challenging but clear course for overcoming the obstacles that stand between prisoners and their freedom. For those behind bars, one goal outshines all others: GETTING OUT! After being released, that goal then shifts to STAYING OUT! This book will help prisoners do both. It has been masterfully constructed into five parts that will help prisoners maximize focus while they strive to accomplish whichever goal is at hand.

MOB$TAR MONEY, $12.00 & $4.00 S/H: After Trey's mother is sent to prison for 75 years to life, he and his little brother are moved from their home in Sacramento, California, to his grandmother's house in Stockton, California where he is forced to find his way in life and become a man on his own in the city's grimy streets. One day, on his way home from the local corner store, Trey has a rough encounter with the neighborhood bully. Luckily, that's when Tyson, a member of the MOBTAR, a local "get money" gang comes to his aid. The two kids quickly become friends, and it doesn't take long before Trey is embraced into the notorious MOB$TAR money gang, which opens the door to an adventure full of sex, money, murder and mayhem that will change his life forever... You will never guess how this story ends!

BLOCK MONEY, $12.00 & $4.00 S/H: Beast, a young thug from the grimy streets of central Stockton, California lives The Block; breathes The Block; and has committed himself to bleed The Block for all it's worth until his very last breath. Then, one day, he meets Nadia; a stripper at the local club who piques his curiosity with her beauty, quick-witted intellect and rider qualities. The problem? She has a man – Esco – a local kingpin with money and power. It doesn't take long, however, before a devious plot is hatched to pull off a heist worth an indeterminable amount of money. Following the acts of treachery, deception and betrayal are twists and turns and a bloody war that will leave you speechless!

HOW TO HUSTLE AND WIN: SEX, MONEY, MURDER EDITION $15.00 & $5.00 S/H: *How To Hu$tle and Win: Sex, Money, Murder Edition* is the grittiest, underground self-help manual for the 21st century street entrepreneur in print. Never has there been such a book written for today's gangsters, goons and go-getters. This self-help handbook is an absolute must-have for anyone who is actively connected to the streets.

RAW LAW: YOUR RIGHTS, & HOW TO SUE WHEN THEY ARE VIOLATED! $15.00 & $5.00 S/H: *Raw Law For Prisoners* is a clear and concise guide for prisoners and their advocates to understanding civil rights laws guaranteed to prisoners under the US Constitution, and how to successfully file a lawsuit when those rights have been violated! From initial complaint to trial, this book will take you through the entire process, step by step, in simple, easy-to-understand terms. Also included are several examples where prisoners have sued prison officials successfully, resulting in changes of unjust rules and regulations and recourse for rights violations, oftentimes resulting in rewards of thousands, even millions of dollars in damages! If you feel your rights have been violated, don't lash out at guards, which is usually ineffective and only makes matters worse. Instead, defend yourself successfully by using the legal system, and getting the power of the courts on your side!

HOW TO WRITE URBAN BOOKS FOR MONEY & FAME: $16.95 & $5.00 S/H: Inside this book you will learn the true story of how Mike Enemigo and King Guru have received money and fame from inside their prison cells by writing urban books; the secrets to writing hood classics so you, too, can be caked up and famous; proper punctuation using hood examples; and resources you can use to achieve your money motivated ambitions! If you're a prisoner who want to write urban novels for money and fame, this must-have manual will give you all the game!

PRETTY GIRLS LOVE BAD BOYS: AN INMATE'S GUIDE TO GETTING GIRLS: $15.00 & $5.00 S/H: Tired of the same, boring, cliché pen pal books that don't tell you what you really need to know? If so, this book is for you! Anything you need to know on the art of long and short distance seduction is included within these pages! Not only does it give you the science of attracting pen pals from websites, it also includes psychological profiles and instructions on how to seduce any woman you set your sights on! Includes interviews of women who have fallen in love with prisoners, bios for pen pal ads, pre-written love letters, romantic poems, love-song lyrics, jokes and much, much more! This book is the ultimate guide – a must-have for any prisoner who refuses to let prison walls affect their MAC'n.

THE LADIES WHO LOVE PRISONERS, $15.00 & $5.00 S/H: New Special Report reveals the secrets of real women who have fallen in love with prisoners, regardless of crime, sentence, or location. This info will give you a HUGE advantage in getting girls from prison.

THE MILLIONAIRE PRISONER: PART 1, $16.95 & $5.00 S/H

THE MILLIONAIRE PRISONER: PART 2, $16.95 & $5.00 S/H

THE MILLIONAIRE PRISONER: SPECIAL 2-IN-1 EDITION, $24.99 & $7.00 S/H: Why wait until you get out of prison to achieve your dreams? Here's a blueprint that you can use to become successful! *The Millionaire Prisoner* is your complete reference to overcoming any obstacle in prison. You won't be able to put it down! With this book you will discover the secrets to: Making money from your cell! Obtain FREE money for correspondence courses! Become an expert on any topic! Develop the habits of the rich! Network with celebrities! Set up your own website! Market your products, ideas and services! Successfully use prison pen pal websites! All of this and much, much more! This book has enabled thousands of prisoners to succeed and it will show you the way also!

THE MILLIONAIRE PRISONER 3: SUCCESS UNIVERSITY, $16.95 & $5 S/H: Why wait until you get out of prison to achieve your dreams? Here's a new-look blueprint that you can use to be successful! *The Millionaire Prisoner 3* contains advanced strategies to overcoming any obstacle in prison. You won't be able to put it down!

THE MILLIONAIRE PRISONER 4: PEN PAL MASTERY, $16.95 & $5 S/H: Tired of subpar results? Here's a master blueprint that you can use to get tons of pen pals! *TMP 4: Pen Pal Mastery* is your complete roadmap to finding your one true love. You won't be able to put it down! With this book you'll DISCOVER the SECRETS to: Get FREE pen pals & which sites are best to use; successful tactics female prisoners can win with; use astrology to find love, friendship & more, build a winning social media presence. All of this and much more!

GET OUT, GET RICH: HOW TO GET PAID LEGALLY WHEN YOU GET OUT OF PRISON!, $16.95 & $5.00 S/H: Many of you are incarcerated for a money-motivated crime. But w/ today's tech & opportunities, not only is the crime-for-money risk/reward ratio not strategically wise, it's not even necessary. You can earn much more money by partaking in any one of the easy, legal hustles explained in this book, regardless of your record. Help yourself earn an honest income so you can not only make a lot of money, but say good-bye to penitentiary chances and prison forever! (Note: Many things in this book can even he done from inside prison.) (ALSO PUBLISHED AS *HOOD MILLIONAIRE: HOW TO HUSTLE AND WIN LEGALLY!*)

THE CEO MANUAL: HOW TO START A BUSINESS WHEN YOU GET OUT OF PRISON, $16.95 & $5.00 S/H: $16.95 & $5 S/H: This new book will teach you the simplest way to start your own business when you get out of prison. Includes:

Start-up Steps! The Secrets to Pulling Money from Investors! How to Manage People Effectively! How To Legally Protect Your Assets from "them"! Hundreds of resources to get you started, including a list of "loan friendly" banks! (ALSO PUBLISHED AS *CEO MANUAL: START A BUSINESS, BE A BOSS!*)

THE MONEY MANUAL: UNDERGROUND CASH SECRETS EXPOSED! 16.95 & $5.00 S/H: Becoming a millionaire is equal parts what you make, and what you don't spend – AKA save. All Millionaires and Billionaires have mastered the art of not only making money, but keeping the money they make (remember Donald Trump's tax maneuvers?), as well as establishing credit so that they are loaned money by banks and trusted with money from investors: AKA OPM – other people's money. And did you know there are millionaires and billionaires just waiting to GIVE money away? It's true! These are all very-little known secrets "they" don't want YOU to know about, but that I'm exposing in my new book!

HOOD MILLIONAIRE; HOW TO HUSTLE & WIN LEGALLY, $16.95 & $5.00 S/H: Hustlin' is a way of life in the hood. We all have money motivated ambitions, not only because we gotta eat, but because status is oftentimes determined by one's own salary. To achieve what we consider financial success, we often invest our efforts into illicit activities – we take penitentiary chances. This leads to a life in and out of prison, sometimes death – both of which are counterproductive to gettin' money. But there's a solution to this, and I have it...

CEO MANUAL: START A BUSINESS BE A BOSS, $16.95 & $5.00 S/H: After the success of the urban-entrepreneur classic *Hood Millionaire: How To Hustle & Win Legally!*, self-made millionaires Mike Enemigo and Sav Hustle team back up to bring you the latest edition of the Hood Millionaire series – *CEO Manual: Start A Business, Be A Boss!* In this latest collection of game laying down the art of "hoodpreneurship", you will learn such things as: 5 Core Steps to Starting Your Own Business! 5 Common Launch Errors You Must Avoid! How To Write a Business Plan! How To Legally Protect Your Assets From "Them"! How To Make Your Business Fundable, Where to Get Money for Your Start-up Business, and even How to Start a Business With No Money! You will learn How to Drive Customers to Your Website, How to Maximize Marketing Dollars, Contract Secrets for the savvy boss, and much, much more! And as an added bonus, we have included over 200 Business Resources, from government agencies and small business development centers, to a secret list of small-business friendly banks that will help you get started!

PAID IN FULL: WELCOME TO DA GAME, $15.00 & $5.00 S/H. In 1983, the movie *Scarface* inspired many kids growing up in America's inner cities to turn their rags into riches by becoming cocaine kingpins. Harlem's Azie Faison was one of them. Faison would ultimately connect with Harlem's Rich Porter and Alpo Martinez, and the trio would go on to become certified street legends of the '80s and early '90s. Years later, Dame Dash and Roc-A-Fella Films would tell their story in the based-on-actual-events movie, *Paid in Full*.

But now, we are telling the story our way – The Cell Block way – where you will get a perspective of the story that the movie did not show, ultimately learning an outcome that you did not expect.

Book one of our series, *Paid in Full: Welcome to da Game*, will give you an inside look at a key player in this story, one that is not often talked about – Lulu, the Columbian cocaine kingpin with direct ties to Pablo Escobar, who plugged Azie in with an unlimited amount of top-tier cocaine at dirt-cheap prices that helped boost the trio to neighborhood superstars and certified kingpin status... until greed, betrayal, and murder destroyed everything....(ALSO PUBLISHED AS *CITY OF GODS*.)

OJ'S LIFE BEHIND BARS, $15.00 & $5 S/H: In 1994, Heisman Trophy winner and NFL superstar OJ Simpson was arrested for the brutal murder of his ex-wife Nicole Brown-Simpson and her friend Ron Goldman. In 1995, after the "trial of the century," he was acquitted of both murders, though most of the world believes he did it. In 2007 OJ was again arrested, but this time in Las Vegas, for armed robbery and kidnapping. On October 3, 2008 he was found guilty sentenced to 33 years and was sent to Lovelock Correctional Facility, in Lovelock, Nevada. There he met inmate-author Vernon Nelson. Vernon was granted a true, insider's perspective into the mind and life of one of the country's most notorious men; one that has never been provided…until now.

THE MOB, $16.99 & $5 S/H: PaperBoy is a Bay Area boss who has invested blood, sweat, and years into building The Mob – a network of Bay Area Street legends, block bleeders, and underground rappers who collaborate nationwide in the interest of pushing a multi-million-dollar criminal enterprise of sex, drugs, and murder.

Based on actual events, little has been known about PaperBoy, the mastermind behind The Mob, and intricate details of its operation, until now.

Follow this story to learn about some of the Bay Area underworld's most glamorous figures and famous events...

AOB, $15.00 & $5 S/H. Growing up in the Bay Area, Manny Fresh the Best had a front-row seat to some of the coldest players to ever do it. And you already know, A.O.B. is the name of the Game! So, When Manny Fresh slides through Stockton one day and sees Rosa, a stupid-bad Mexican chick with a whole lotta 'talent' behind her walking down the street tryna get some money, he knew immediately what he had to do: Put it In My Pocket!

AOB 2, $15.00 & $5 S/H.

AOB 3, $15.00 & $5 S/H.

PIMPOLOGY: THE 7 ISMS OF THE GAME, $15.00 & $5 S/H: It's been said that if you knew better, you'd do better. So, in the spirit of dropping jewels upon the rare few who truly want to know how to win, this collection of exclusive Game has been compiled. And though a lot of so-called players claim to know how the Pimp Game is supposed to go, none have revealed the real. . . Until now!

JAILHOUSE PUBLISHING FOR MONEY, POWER & FAME: $24.99 & $7 S/H: In 2010, after flirting with the idea for two years, Mike Enemigo started writing his first book. In 2014, he officially launched his publishing company, The Cell Block, with the release of five books. Of course, with no mentor(s), how-to guides, or any real resources, he was met with failure after failure as he tried to navigate the treacherous goal of publishing books from his prison cell. However, he was determined to make it. He was determined to figure it out and he refused to quit. In Mike's new book, *Jailhouse Publishing for Money, Power, and Fame*, he breaks down all his jailhouse publishing secrets and strategies, so you can do all he's done, but without the trials and tribulations he's had to go through...

KITTY KAT, ADULT ENTERTAINMENT RESOURCE BOOK, $24.99 & $7.00 S/H: This book is jam packed with hundreds of sexy non nude photos including photo spreads. The book contains the complete info on sexy photo sellers, hot magazines, page turning bookstore, sections on strip clubs, porn stars, alluring models, thought provoking stories and must-see movies.

PRISON LEGAL GUIDE, $24.99 & $7.00 S/H: The laws of the U.S. Judicial system are complex, complicated, and always growing and changing. Many prisoners spend days on end digging through its intricacies. Pile on top of the legal code the rules and regulations of a correctional facility, and you can see how high the deck is being stacked against you. Correct legal information is the key to your survival when you have run afoul of the system (or it is running afoul of you). Whether you are an accomplished jailhouse lawyer helping newbies learn the ropes, an old head fighting bare-knuckle for your rights in the courts, or a hustler just looking to beat the latest write-up – this book has something for you!

PRISON HEALTH HANDBOOK, $19.99 & $7.00 S/H: *The Prison Health Handbook* is your one-stop go-to source for information on how to maintain your best health while inside the American prison system. Filled with information, tips, and secrets from doctors, gurus, and other experts, this book will educate you on such things as proper workout and exercise regimens; yoga benefits for prisoners; how to meditate effectively; pain management tips; sensible dieting solutions; nutritional knowledge; an understanding of various cancers, diabetes, hepatitis, and other diseases all too common in prison; how to effectively deal with mental health issues such as stress, PTSD, anxiety, and depression; a list of things your doctors DON'T want YOU to know; and much, much more!

All books are available on thecellblock.net website.

You can also order by sending a money order or institutional check to:

The Cell Block; PO Box 1025; Rancho Cordova, CA 95741

PRISON RIOT RADIO

Industry reps want to hear you!

Are you a rapper? We will upload your freestyles to our website, prisonriotradio.com, FREE for top industry execs to hear!

Pick up the phone and become a star!

We will record you on the phone! All raw freestyles will be recorded FREE. If you need a recording and a beat, the prices are below...

$25 Per Recording

$150 For 8 Recordings

$30 Per Beat

$10 For Cover Art

We accept songs, spoken word, podcasts and interviews! Learn the game and how to get your money!

For more information, to send material, or to set up a phone recording session, email prisonriotradio@gmail.com or jayrene@prisonriotradio@gmail.com.

Made in the USA
Columbia, SC
29 September 2024

43267992R00174